Organic

and P~~ulses~~

Edited by

D. Younie and B.R. Taylor
SAC, Craibstone Estate, Bucksburn, Aberdeen, AB21 9YA

J.P. Welch
Elm Farm Research Centre, Hamstead Marshall, Newbury, Berkshire RG20 0HR

and

J.M. Wilkinson
School of Biology, University of Leeds, Leeds LS2 9JT

Papers presented at conferences held at the Heriot-Watt University, Edinburgh, and at Cranfield University Silsoe Campus, Bedfordshire, 6 and 9 November 2001.
Organised by David Younie and James Welch

Sponsored by

First published in Great Britain by
Chalcombe Publications
Painshall, Church Lane, Welton,
Lincoln, LN2 3LT
United Kingdom

ISBN 0 948617 47 0

Printed in Great Britain by Booksprint, Wellington, Somerset

Contents

Page

Foreword   v

Chapter 1   **The market for organic cereals
             and pulses**
             B. Wilburn   1

Chapter 2   **Choice of species and varieties**
             B.R. Taylor and W. F. Cormack   9

Chapter 3   **Species and varietal mixtures**
             M. S. Wolfe   29

Chapter 4   **Rotations and nutrient management
             strategies**
             L. Phillips, S.K. Huxham, S.R. Briggs
             and D. L. Sparkes   51

Chapter 5   **Weed control in organic cereals and pulses**
             D.H.K. Davies and J. P. Welch   77

Chapter 6   **Maintaining grain quality:
             Milling, malting and feed**
             M.F.F. Carver and B.R. Taylor   115

Chapter 7   **Producing high quality seed**
             J. E. Thomas and R. Wyartt   135

Chapter 8   **Commercial farm case studies: cereals**
             J.M. Sharman and R. Steele   147

Chapter 9   **Commercial farm case study: pulses**
             D. Wilson   165

Foreword

DAVID YOUNIE

*SAC Agronomy Department, Craibstone Estate, Bucksburn,
Aberdeen AB21 9YA*

At the threshold of the 21st century, concerns have increased about the way our food is produced - in terms of external inputs, environmental impact and animal welfare. The rapid expansion in sales of organic food is a testament to these concerns. At the same time there has been rapid expansion in the area of land managed organically in the United Kingdom. However, this expansion has been largely in the livestock sector. The arable sector has been slow to expand, but there is a considerable need for more crop output to meet both the consumer demand for organic crop products and the need for feedingstuffs by the livestock industry. One of the reasons for the relatively slow rate of expansion in the arable sector has been the lack of technical information to support converting farmers. This book is intended to address this deficiency.

In conventional agriculture, cereal production is characterised by reliance on a wide range of external inputs such as soluble fertilisers, herbicides, fungicides and insecticides. This is the direct, or reactive, approach to crop husbandry. Given this degree of reliance on external inputs, it is not surprising that conventional farmers find it hard to envisage how it is possible to grow organic cereals.

Organic farming requires a completely different approach. The converting farmer needs to adopt a new mind set. This involves the management of the ecosystem in the soil and in the crop - to manage nutrient availability to the crop and to minimise the impact of weeds, pests and diseases. Essentially this is a preventative or anticipatory approach to crop husbandry rather than a reactive approach. In this way the organic farmer works **with** the natural system rather than seeking to dominate it. There are, of course, some direct approaches which are available to the organic farmer, such as mechanical weed control. Likewise many of the techniques used in organic grain production are also applicable to conventional production and could help to improve margins for conventional producers.

The book contains the papers presented at two conferences held in November 2001, organised by SAC and Elm Farm Research Centre. Experienced researchers and advisers, together with leading farmers, have been brought together to provide a comprehensive overview of the state of the art in organic cereal and pulse production. This guide will provide farmers with an invaluable resource for enhancing the profitability of organic grain production.

Chapter 1

The Market for Organic Cereals and Pulses

B. WILBURN

Gleadell Agriculture Ltd, Lindsey House, Hemswell Cliff, Gainsborough, Lincolnshire DN21 5TH

CHANGES IN ORGANIC CROPPING AREAS

The area of organic and in-conversion land in the UK has increased greatly over recent years, most strikingly between April 1999 and April 2000, rising from 240,000 ha to 416,000 ha, an increase of 70%. Of the fully organic land area 10% is arable, 3% horticulture and fruit, 17% temporary ley, and 70% permanent pasture and rough grazing (Soil Association, 2001).

The area of organically-managed arable crops in the UK exceeds 10,000 ha. Projections for future areas of cereals and pulses based on expected seed usage (Soil Association Seed Working Group, unpublished figures) are shown in Table 1.1. The total area could rise to over 50,000 ha by 2004 with wheat still dominating the cereal area, followed by oats and then barley, with combining peas and field beans remaining minor crops. These figures may differ from other estimates since they do not take account of yearly distortions due to weather or the use of home-saved seed.

Large increases in crop outputs might be expected to have profound effects on prices of organic cereals and pulses, but this has not been the experience so far. Many EU countries have a higher proportion of land in organic production than the UK, but are still net importers of organic grain (HGCA, 2000) and have price premiums for organic grain over non-organic grain similar to those in the UK. In Germany, where a greater proportion of land is devoted to organic production than in the UK, although the price of organic milling wheat has fallen from about £300/tonne in 1993 to under £200/tonne in 2000, in real terms it has remained between 2 and 3 times that of the conventional milling wheat price.

Table 1.1. **Projected areas of organically-managed cereals and pulses, 2000 to 2004 (ha)**

Species	2000	2001	2002	2003	2004
Wheat	6,353	11,228	16,377	23,654	32,279
Barley	1,152	2,014	2,926	4,339	5,915
Oats	1,782	3,386	5,078	7,872	11,021
Rye	277	486	706	1,051	1,435
Triticale	420	737	1,071	1,593	2,174
Peas	28	49	71	106	145
Beans	251	440	640	953	1301
Totals	**10,263**	**18,340**	**26,869**	**39,568**	**54,270**

ORGANIC PRODUCTION

It is expected that organic arable production will increase steadily over the next few years. Consumer demand has forced supermarkets to stock more organic produce than ever before and this has resulted in a major increase in raw materials required for processing. Cereal and pulse production increased by 82,000 tonnes between 1999 and 2001 (own data), but consumption of arable crops is still at least 65% greater than current production with the difference being met by imports. With the concerns over genetically-modified organisms (GMOs) and stricter controls on feeding standards for organic livestock, the demand for organic cereals and pulses has never been greater.

Soil Association (2001) estimates for the production of organic cereals and pulses for 1999 are given in Table 1.2. Wheat is the most valuable arable crop for organic growers in the UK. Of nearly 19,000 tonnes grown in 1999, just under half was used for milling. This is a strong market with demand likely to exceed supply for the foreseeable future provided that quality specifications, and protein levels in particular, can be met.

Some 8,000 tonnes of organic oats were produced in the UK in 1999, of which 80% was used for livestock feed. As more livestock than arable land is converted to organic production, the demand for feed grains is likely to remain strong or increase. In addition there is increasing interest and demand for organic oats from many of the breakfast cereal manufacturers.

Table 1.2.   Estimated production and value of organic arable crops harvested in the UK in 1999 (Soil Association, 2001)

Crop	Production (tonnes)	Value (£m)
Milling wheat	9,000	1.80
Feed wheat	9,700	1.75
Milling oats	1,600	0.30
Feed oats	6,400	0.95
Processing/malting barley	1,000	0.19
Feed barley	3,800	0.67
Triticale	2,200	0.37
Rye	800	0.13
Spelt	400	0.05
Beans	2,400	0.47
Peas	300	0.05

A similar percentage of organic barley is fed on farm, with just over 20% being processed, mostly for malt. The organic malting barley market is at present under supplied, but organic beers and sprits are a relatively small market, which is difficult to predict in the UK. Until the malting market becomes more established, the main outlet for organic barley is likely to be for livestock feed.

Triticale suits organic systems (on marginal, lighter soils in particular) and has increased in production more than other organic cereals in recent years. It is a good quality feed grain, which can also produce large amounts of straw. Of the other cereals, rye and spelt are produced for niche markets and should only be grown on contract.

The production of beans exceeds that of combining peas, which are more difficult to grow organically. As demand for organic protein increases, so the demand for home-grown pulses is likely to remain strong. This may also encourage organic livestock farmers to look at other protein-producing crops for their rotations. The expressed cake of oilseed rape is high in protein, but lack of supply has prevented UK crushers from offering buy-back contracts to growers. As it is more convenient and cheaper for crushers to source home-grown material than to import, a UK supply would be preferred. This market, therefore, has great potential, and should be encouraged by crushers and producers alike.

MARKET REQUIREMENTS

Specifications for organic grain are similar to those for non-organic grain but growers generally achieve the required specifications without difficulty. However, organic crops may require more attention to husbandry details than conventional crops in order to produce an acceptable sample for a premium market. For example, growers may not realise the importance of correct storage procedures for the maintenance of germination levels of malting barley or the effect that weed seeds can have on grain specific weights.

Specialist buy-back contracts are offered on a number of organic crops including wheat for milling and biscuit-making wheat, malting barley, oats for milling, and pulses (combining peas and field beans). Details of the required specifications are shown below.

Milling Wheat

Premium over feed	£20/t
Minimum protein	11.9% of DM[1]
Minimum Hagberg falling number	250
Minimum specific weight	76 kg/hl
Maximum moisture content	15%

[1] Dry matter

Biscuit Wheat

Premium over feed	£10/t
Maximum protein	12.5% of DM
Minimum Hagberg falling number	180
Minimum specific weight	74 kg/hl
Maximum moisture content	15%

Malting Barley

Premium over feed	£20/t
Nitrogen basis	1.65% of DM
Minimum specific weight	64 kg/hl
Maximum moisture content	15%
Maximum screenings	5%
Minimum germination	97%

Milling Oats

Premium over feed	£20/t
Mininimum specific weight	50 kg/hl
Maximum moisture content	15%

Maximum screenings	6%
Must be of good colour	

Pulses

Maximum moisture content	15%
Maximum admixture	2%
Must be of merchantable quality	

The main traded varieties of cereals and pulses are shown in Table 1.3. These represent a wide range of variety types: wheat varieties are aimed mainly at the quality milling market; barley varieties are predominantly for feed.

Table 1.3. Commonly traded organic varieties of cereals and pulses.

Crop	Main varieties
Winter wheat	Hereward, Spark, Maris Widgeon, Malacca, Shamrock, Deben, Claire, Petrus, Consort
Spring wheat	Axona, Paragon, Chablis, Imp
Winter barley	Pearl, Regina, Jewel
Spring barley	Chariot, Dandy, Hart, Optic, Chalice
Winter oats	Aintree, Solva, Gerald, Dunkeld, Jalna, Millennium
Spring oats	Melys, Drummer, Winston, Banquo, Firth
Triticale	Purdy, Trimaran, Binova, Ego, Olympus, Partout, Taurus
Rye	Humbolt, Merkator, Admiral
Combining peas	Grafila, Elan, Eiffel, Nitouche, and forage pea varieties
Winter field beans	Bourdon, Punch, Target, Striker, Clipper, Silver
Spring field beans	Scirocco, Victor, Mars, Quattro, Picadilly

CONCLUSIONS

- Large increases in the areas of organic cereals and pulses are predicted.
- Market specifications are similar for both organically-produced and conventionally-produced grain.
- Organic milling wheat is in deficit partly because quality requirements are difficult to meet.
- The organic market for malting barley has good potential for further growth.
- Demand for organic cereals and pulses for livestock feed will remain strong for the foreseeable future.
- Organic cereal and pulse premiums are likely to be maintained, as demand continues to outstrip supply.
- GMOs, food scares and health issues will ensure that organic protein (derived from pulses and oilseeds) remains in very strong demand.

REFERENCES

HGCA (2000). Organic Farming - the next step. *HGCA MI Prospects*, 2 (19), 4-5.

Soil Association (2001). *The Organic Food and Farming Report 2000*. The Soil Association, Bristol.

Chapter 2

Choice of Species and Varieties

B.R. TAYLOR[1] and W. F. CORMACK[2]

[1]*SAC Agronomy Department, Ferguson Building, Craibstone Estate, Bucksburn, Aberdeen AB21 9YA*
[2]*ADAS Terrington, Terrington St Clement, King's Lynn, Norfolk PE34 4PW*

CEREALS

All the main cereal crops - wheat, barley and oats, triticale, rye and spelt - can be grown organically in the UK. The areas of cereals grown to organic standards in the UK in 1998 and 1999 are given in Table 2.1. The total area of cereals is expected to more than double by 2002 (Taylor *et al.*, 2001).

Table 2.1. **UK organic cereal area (ha) 1998 and 1999**
(Soil Association, 2001)

	1998	1999
Wheat	4163	4320
Barley	1005	1200
Oats	1949	1900
Triticale	324	500
Rye	147	200
Spelt	61	100
Total	**7649**	**8220**

Until recently, the most important organic cereals were wheat and oats, with premiums paid for samples which reached milling quality. In the last year or two, more livestock farmers than arable farmers have converted to organic production so that feed grain has been in short supply, and the range of cereals grown organically has increased. New markets have also developed. Malted organic barley has been used for some time to produce beer: now barley malt and wheat have been processed into organic whisky.

Organic growers may use different criteria to those of conventional growers when selecting which cereal to grow. Important considerations include available markets, soil type, the preferred time of sowing, ability to compete with weeds, disease resistance, and rotational position, particularly in relation to nitrogen supply. Winter cereals yield more and are harvested earlier than spring cereals but are unlikely to take up all the mineralised N available in autumn (Watson, 1993).

Where spring cereals are grown, land should not be ploughed until late winter in order to minimise leaching of mineralised nitrogen. Spring-sown cereals have a lower nutrient demand, are less exposed to weed competition because of their shorter growing period, and are more suitable for undersowing with grass/clover or clover. The pattern of soil nitrogen release corresponds better to the nitrogen demands of spring cereals than winter cereals. However, on nutrient retentive soils such as silty clay loams, where winter leaching of nitrogen is lower, this is less of a concern and winter-sown cereals will generally yield more. These heavier soils are also less suited to spring cropping particularly in drier areas where establishment can be poor resulting in uncompetitive crops with a lot of weeds. Spring cereals in these areas are best limited to the end of the rotation for undersowing. The ability to compete with weeds is greater in oats and triticale than in barley, and least in modern wheat varieties (Welsh *et al.*, 2001). As a result, oats and triticale may be less well suited to undersowing, particularly in high-fertility situations.

Organic wheat is grown for feed and for milling for bread, biscuits and flour. Current prices are distorted by the shortage of UK-grown feed grains. Feed wheat sells for as much as £185/tonne while the best high-protein milling samples can attract prices of over £195/tonne (Barrington *et al*, 2001). Protein standards are particularly difficult to achieve with organically grown wheat, a reflection of the lower nitrogen supply, particularly later in growth, compared with non-organic crops. Winter wheat is potentially the highest yielding cereal for organic situations and is often the most suitable cereal to follow a fertility-building phase in the rotation. In the most favourable situations, i.e. with adequate nitrogen supply, yields of over 8.0 t/ha can be achieved (Cormack, 1997). Spring wheats do not yield as well as winter varieties but are generally of higher quality. In northern areas of the UK, spring wheat does not mature until mid or late September when adverse weather conditions can reduce grain quality. Where winter conditions are not likely to be severe, some varieties of spring wheat, e.g. Axona, sown in November, will give higher grain protein contents than true winter varieties but yields are likely to be less. Spring varieties tiller less than winter varieties and are less able to compete with weeds.

Barley is earlier to mature and, with its greater tillering capacity, competes better with weeds than wheat, but it generally yields less. Organically grown barley is mainly used for animal feed but smaller amounts are malted or processed for human consumption. Yield can range from 2.5 to 6.0 t/ha depending principally, as for wheat, on the effects of soil type and rotational position on nitrogen supply.

Contracts for malting barley are available with the market generally under supplied. There is less experience of organic winter barley than spring barley in the UK. Winter barley has the advantage that the ground is ploughed and worked when soil conditions are generally more favourable, and mineralised nitrogen is available to assist crop establishment. Disadvantages of autumn sowing are a greater risk from Barley Yellow Dwarf Virus (BYDV) if the crop is established early or is sown after a ley, and a high susceptibility of many varieties to at least one commonly occurring disease.

Winter barley is sown earlier than other winter cereals and is more exposed to weed competition than spring barley. Since barley yield depends more than in other cereals on adequate tillering and ear numbers, soil nitrogen availability in early spring is critical; organic growers may have to apply manures to meet this demand. Spring barley, on the other hand, is generally less affected by disease. It has the disadvantage of being very sensitive to adverse soil conditions caused by cultivations in the winter or spring when conditions are wet. However, spring barley provides more opportunity for weed control cultivations before sowing because of the longer time available. This is especially true for grass weeds such as couch.

Organic oats can be grown for feed or milling for which there is an additional premium although the market is smaller than for wheat or barley. Oats have a lower nitrogen requirement than wheat or barley and should not be grown in high fertility situations because of the risk of lodging and late ripening. High soil fertility can be exploited better by crops such as wheat, potatoes or brassicas. A crop of oats is a good competitor with weeds and this can be used to good effect following a crop that is a poor competitor, for example swedes or carrots. Oats might also follow wheat or barley.

Spring oats can be undersown with a grass/clover mixture when it is usually necessary to reduce the seed rate. Winter oats are sown at about the same time as winter barley and like winter barley are susceptible to BYDV. They are less winter hardy than other winter cereals and should not be sown on exposed northerly sites. Although susceptible to weed competition in the early stages, winter oats are long-strawed and compete well with weeds. However, lodging can be a problem and highly fertile sites such as those after grass/clover leys should be avoided.

Triticale is a useful crop for organic systems. It has long straw, making it competitive against weeds, good disease resistance, and a greater tolerance of drought than wheat. Furthermore, it appears to be less palatable to rabbits than other cereals. Triticale performs relatively well under conditions of low fertility which makes it more suitable as a second cereal than winter wheat. The price of triticale is competitive with other organic cereals grown as feed grain. Although only winter varieties exist it is possible to plant triticale through to the end of January/early February if soil conditions allow.

Spelt is an old cereal with new interest. It is winter-sown and can perform well in severe conditions though not necessarily in poor environments. It shows good disease resistance and competes well with weeds. The harvested grain requires special milling to remove the hull. There is a very limited market and crops should only be grown under contract.

Constraints imposed by crop-specific fertiliser and chemical applications on the use of crop species mixtures (mixed crops, alternate rows, alternate strips) that limit their application in non-organic situations, do not apply on organic farms. Crop species mixtures may have a number of advantages in organic farming including reductions in pest and disease levels, improved weed control and provision of nitrogen where legumes are used in continuous systems. Wheat and beans do not compete for nitrogen when grown together such that higher protein levels may be achieved in wheat grown with beans than in wheat alone (Bulson *et al.*, 1997).

Cereal varieties

Information on cereal varieties is available in the UK from various sources including NIAB, SAC, DARD, the advisory services, merchants, end-users and the trade. Detailed comparative information is contained in the NIAB Cereals Variety Handbook, the SAC Cereal Recommended List and the DARD List of Cereal Recommended Varieties for Northern Ireland. These publications include comparisons of varieties grown without fungicides and plant growth regulators rather than under organic conditions. They do provide some guide to performance under organic cultivation but need to be used with care, principally as the trial plots are grown with a non-limiting nutrient supply.

In contrast, most organic systems have a much lower nutrient availability, particularly of nitrogen which is the main driver of yield and which also interacts with weed and disease levels. Since 2000 harvest, three series of organic variety trials are underway; by NIAB funded by plant breeders, by Elm Farm Research Centre and by Arable Research Centres funded by HGCA as project 2237. Results from the 2000 NIAB trials were included in the 2001 Cereals Variety Handbook (NIAB, 2000a).

Variety probably has less influence on cereal yield and profitability in organic compared with non-organic situations due to the greater variation in nutrient availability, and weed, pest and disease levels in organic systems. Organic growers may be expected to use different criteria to those used by conventional growers when selecting cereal varieties, and there is evidence that the best performing conventional varieties do not always transfer well to organic systems (Fenwick, 2000). For organic systems, growers should choose varieties that perform well in trials on organic farms. However, as this data remains very limited, the alternative is to use the untreated controls in non-organic trials as a guide.

Regressions of variety yields in one year's organic trials on the yields of the same varieties in long-term non-organic untreated trials published by NIAB (2000a), show significant positive relationships for winter wheat and spring and winter barley, but little evidence of yield correlations for spring wheat or spring oats, and a possible negative relationship for winter oats (Figure 1.1).

In general, varieties should be chosen which have high grain yields, high scores for resistance to appropriate diseases, and long straw since this may confer good competitive ability against weeds, especially in the less competitive cereals such as wheat. Other characteristics are important for specific markets, locations and farm situations. Malting and milling markets require specific varieties, good straw strength is important where a crop is to be grown after a long grass/clover ley, resistance to ear-loss is important in exposed fields, and early maturity reduces harvesting risks in northerly and upland situations.

For premium markets, selection of an appropriate variety is essential. Conventional bread-milling varieties of wheat can achieve acceptable grain quality under organic conditions, but in most cases protein content, at 9% to 10%, is likely to be significantly lower than non-organic expectations. The choice of varieties for this market is limited but high grain protein and Hagberg Falling Number (HFN) are essential. Similarly, variety choice might be influenced by level

Figure 1.1. Comparison of cereal yields in 2000 from one year's organic and long-term non-organic trials untreated with pesticides or growth regulators (for cultivars common to both trial series). (Source: NIAB 2000a)

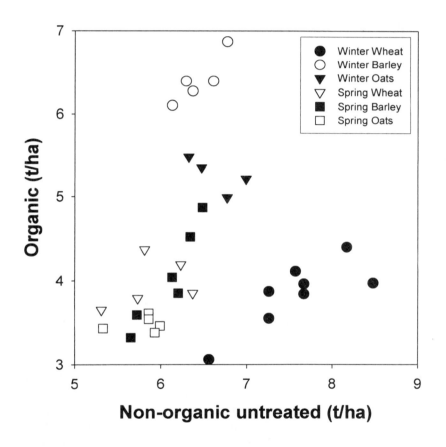

of screenings in malting barley, and specific weight where feed grain is intended for sale. This is dealt with elsewhere in this publication. One variety is rarely the obvious best choice for any given situation and growers have to weigh strengths and weaknesses for different characters. For example, comparing bread-milling winter wheat varieties, Hereward has longer straw and higher grain protein but lower HFN, and is more at risk from mildew and yellow rust, whilst Malacca has better foliar disease resistance and HFN, but lower grain protein and specific weight, and shorter straw (Table 2 2).

Table 2. 2. **Characteristics of winter wheat varieties grown in a non-organic situation** (from NIAB, 2000a)

	Hereward	Malacca
Untreated yield (% of treated controls)	72	72
Shortness of straw	7	8
Resistance to mildew	6	7
Resistance to yellow rust	7	9
Resistance to brown rust	8	8
Resistance to *Septoria nodorum*	7	7
Resistance to *Septoria tritici*	6	6
Protein content (%)	13.2	12.3
Hagberg Falling Number	267	346
Specific weight (kg/hl)	79.2	75.9

If, in future, breeders cannot guarantee their material free from genetically manipulated parents, the choice of varieties for organic growers will become very limited, encouraging the development of breeding programmes dedicated to organic varieties. It is probable that such varieties will be selected for different criteria to those for which conventional varieties are selected under conditions of high fertiliser and agrochemical inputs. Whilst some desirable characteristics are common to varieties under both systems, e.g. disease resistance, selection criteria for varieties to be grown under organic conditions might include objectives not thought relevant to non-organic systems. This could include competition with weeds, resistance to a different range of pests and diseases, the ability to perform in crop mixtures, or the ability to make better use of lower levels of soil nitrogen

It is not appropriate to reproduce here tables of recommended varieties for the range of cereal species grown in the UK. However, examples of cereal varieties suitable for organic rotations, with the criteria used in their selection are shown in Table 2.3. The list is by no means exhaustive and growers must decide which criteria to use in their own situations. Other varieties may be more suitable in specific situations.

There are a number of traditional varieties used in organic farming, of which the winter wheat Maris Widgeon is a good example. Maris Widgeon can give good hard-milling samples although the HFN is not as high as that of modern milling varieties. It has long straw which commands a premium for thatching if handled carefully (this may mean harvesting by binder!). Until recently there was little information to compare Maris Widgeon with modern varieties of winter wheat but trials in 2000 conducted by the Arable Research Centres and Elm Farm Research Centre indicated that yields (4.0-4.9 t/ha) are comparable to modern varieties under organic conditions.

For organic growers, variety mixtures offer a number of positive benefits over single varieties. Varieties suitable for inclusion in mixtures may be different to those suitable for use in pure stands. Mixtures are considered elsewhere in this publication.

PULSES

Pulses are legume seeds, normally sown as field crops and harvested by combine harvester. The range of species grown in the UK includes winter and spring varieties of field beans (*Vicia faba*), peas (*Pisum sativa*), lupins (*Lupinus* spp.), and specialised crops such as

Table 2.3. Examples of cereal varieties for organic rotations

Cereal	Market	Variety	Characteristics
Winter wheat	Feed	Deben	Good resistance to yellow rust and *Septoria*, high untreated and organic yield, tall straw but rather weak, and below average resistance to mildew.
Winter wheat	Bread-milling	Hereward	Longer straw than other main bread-milling varieties, but good straw strength. Reasonable disease resistance. High protein but lower HFN and lower yield than other recommended varieties in untreated trials.
Spring wheat	Bread-milling	Paragon	Good bread-making quality and disease resistance. Long straw of average strength. High untreated yield in untreated trials but lower yield than Chablis in organic trials
Winter oats	Milling	Kingfisher	Long straw, good disease resistance and large grain. Early ripening and high yield, but some lodging risk.
Spring oats	Milling	Firth	High untreated yield, good mildew resistance and straw strength, but shorter than average
Winter barley	Feed	Pearl	Long, strong straw and bold grain with good yield and disease resistance, but later than average.
Spring barley	Malting	Chariot	Long straw, good mildew resistance and relatively early, but susceptible to *Rhynchosporium*. Well-tried variety but yield is below average.
Spring barley	Feed	Riviera	Tall stiff, straw. Large grain, good resistance to mildew and average resistance to *Rhynchosporium*. Good yield.
Triticale	Feed	Ego	Tall, stiff-strawed with high yield potential and good specific weight

lentils (*Lens esculenta*) and soya beans (*Glycine max*). Peas and beans are the most commonly grown pulses in the UK. In 1999 there were 200 ha of peas and 680 ha of field beans grown organically in the UK (Soil Association, 2001); organic peas and field beans are currently worth £220/t and £210/t respectively (Barrington *et al*, 2001).

The main use of pulses is as animal feed although peas, and to a lesser extent beans, may be used for human consumption. Interest in protein crops increases when the supplies of imported soya are threatened or, as recently, cannot be guaranteed free of genetically-modified material. A comparison of the nutritive values of pulses is given in Table 2.4. Beans have a higher protein content than peas and are similar in energy value. Recent interest in lupins has been stimulated by their high protein content and feed value which is comparable to soya (Acamovic, 2001).

Table 2.4. **Comparative nutritive value of pulses** (from Ewing, 1997)

	Dry matter (DM,%)	Crude protein (% of DM)	ME – ruminants (MJ/kg DM)	ME – poultry (MJ/kg DM)
Beans	86.0	29.0	14.0	13.5
Peas	86.0	26.0	13.6	13,0
Lupin flakes	86.0	32.0	14.5	11.0

Pulse yields do not depend on applied nitrogen as manure or fertiliser. As in all legumes, nitrogen is supplied from root nodules in which *Rhizobium* spp. bacteria convert soil atmospheric nitrogen into a form usable by the plant. The amount of N fixed in the roots of grain legumes has been estimated at 150 to 200 kg/ha, most of which is removed in the grain of the crop (Fisher, 1996). Because soil organic matter breakdown and nitrate mineralisation continue during crop growth, there remains a residue of N in the soil, greater than after non-legumes. This is equivalent to 40 to 50 kg N/ha, and is an important contribution to maintaining soil fertility in organic systems, particularly in stockless rotations (Cormack, 1997).

Field beans may be autumn (winter) or spring sown. Winter beans have large seed (500 to 600g/1000 seeds) and are sown from late October to mid November in the UK. Winter beans can be sown to a depth of 8 to 10 cm but establishment can be conveniently done by broadcasting and ploughing-in the seed to a depth of 12 to 15 cm in order to establish about 25 plants/m^2 (Lampkin and Measures, 2001). Spring beans should be sown as soon as soil conditions allow in February or March, although later sowings, up to early April, can still give acceptable yields. They have smaller seed (350 to 500g/1000 seeds) and the target plant population is 40 to 50 plants/m^2.

Spring beans are sometimes regarded as a risky crop, requiring a dry period for sowing in February/March followed by wetter conditions for germination, adequate moisture for growth, and a dry late summer for ripening and harvest. They branch less than winter beans and in order to achieve a rapid, uniform establishment they should be sown and not ploughed in (Knott *et al.*, 1994).

The relatively large seed of both winter and spring beans may require modifications to the seed drill, such as special feed wheels, to avoid cracking the seed. Beans are relatively slow to emerge despite their large seed size. This, and the low densities at which they are sown compared to other arable crops, leaves bean crops open to potentially damaging weed competition in the early stages of growth. Using a harrow comb on the emerged crop may be possible or the crop may be sown in wide rows to allow inter-row cultivations (Rasmussen *et al.*, 2000).

Field beans are normally harvested later than cereals. Winter-sown varieties mature earlier than spring varieties in southern parts of the UK and may be harvested from early/mid August onwards, but where adequate moisture is available to maintain slower growth in northern areas harvest may be delayed until mid or late October, making winter beans an unsuitable choice for Scotland (SAC, 2000). Spring varieties reach maturity in late August or early September in the southern UK, but a month later in the north, where they are combined before winter beans. Unlike combining peas, field beans generally remain standing until harvest; they are less affected by wet weather and less likely to shed than peas if harvest is delayed.

Yields of non-organic winter beans may be above those of spring beans in the south (NIAB, 2000b) but are unlikely to exceed spring beans in the north. Since winter beans are also more likely to suffer from the chocolate spot disease than spring beans (Knott *et al.*, 1994), there would appear to be little advantage in organic situations from winter beans which provide very little winter ground cover against erosion, weed development or nutrient loss.

Combining peas are less common than field beans in organic rotations, mainly due to concerns about lodging and weed control. Peas may be autumn or spring-sown, although at present the winter crop is not well developed in the UK. Spring combining peas are sown in March or early April. Seed size varies from 150 to 350g/1000 seeds, and seed is normally sown with a cereal drill to establish 60 to 90 plants/m^2 (Biddle *et al.*, 1988).

Because peas may lodge severely, allowing weed growth in the crop before harvest, good weed control is essential under organic conditions where pre-harvest chemical desiccation is not possible. Peas, like beans, are relatively widely spaced, are slow to emerge, and are not good at suppressing early weed growth. Weed control in winter peas may be especially difficult since soil conditions after sowing are unlikely to be suitable for mechanical weeding. In spring, mechanical methods of weed control such as cultivation with a harrow comb in the emerged crop may be successful, although limited evidence is available from the UK.

Wherever possible, combining peas should be sown in fields where weeds are not a problem. Other cultural methods of weed control, such as increased seed rate, will reduce early competition from weeds, but may exacerbate crop lodging (Taylor *et al.*, 1991). In favourable areas spring varieties are harvested in August; three to four weeks earlier than field beans. Under conventional conditions yields are similar from spring and winter sown combining pea crops, and may be expected to exceed those from beans.

Lupins are a minor crop in the UK. Past attempts to grow lupins in the UK have resulted in extremely late harvests (after Christmas not being unusual) but more determinate varieties are now on offer. Lupin species differ in flower colour and leaf type: white (*Lupinus albus*), yellow (*Lupinus luteus*) and blue or narrow-leaved (*Lupinus angustifolius*). Varieties are available for winter and spring sowing although the areas most suited to each have yet to be determined in practice. Lupins prefer more acidic soils than those suited to peas or beans, normally below about pH 6, and this, coupled with an ability of some lupin species to take up phosphorus efficiently, may make them adapted to low-fertility sites.

Winter lupins are sown in late August or early September and the stage of crop development reached before winter is critical for winter survival (Shield *et al.*, 2000). Spring lupins are sown in March or April. The aim is to establish 28 to 30 plants/m^2 for winter lupins and 90 to100 plant/m^2 for spring lupins (Impey, 2001); seed should be inoculated with *Bradyrhizobium* spp. immediately before sowing. Neither winter nor spring lupins are very competitive with weeds and the comparatively early sowing date of the winter crop is very likely to require autumn weed control. Lupins remain standing until harvest and late weed development is less of a problem than in peas.

Grain yields from lupins are reported to be from 2 to 4 t/ha. Harvest dates range from mid-August for spring-sown narrow-leaved varieties in the south of England (Anon, 2001), to October onwards for spring-sown white lupins in northern Scotland. In trials at three sites in the southern UK winter varieties were harvested after spring types and were taller and higher yielding (NIAB, 2000b). Winter lupins are unlikely to be suitable for Scotland. There is no established market for lupins though the quality of the crop would indicate that it could be more valuable than peas or beans.

Pulse varieties

A recommended list of combining pea and field bean varieties is published by NIAB (2000b) and includes data from lupin trials. SAC (2000) publishes an annual list of recommended combining pea varieties. Data in these lists is from trials carried out under non-organic conditions. Field beans differ in seed yield, plant height, ripening date, resistance to lodging and disease, seed size and protein content, and flower colour (indicating seed tannin content). Four winter and twelve spring bean varieties are recommended by NIAB for 2001. These include the white-flowered varieties Silver (winter- sown), Alpine and Avon.

Although tannin-free (white-flowered) beans may be fed to monogastric animals at higher rates than beans containing tannin, there is no additional premium for them whether non-organic or organically produced. Not only are white-flowered varieties reputed to have thinner seed coats than other varieties (Bulson, 1993), but tannin is also thought to act as a natural fungicide which protects the germinating seed from soil-borne diseases (e.g. *Fusarium* spp.), so that tannin-free varieties may show poor establishment under organic conditions; this does not appear to be the case in non-organic crops (Knott *et al.*, 1994). Since white-flowered varieties also tend to be short, organic growers have no reason to choose these instead of coloured-flowered varieties.

The most important considerations for organic growers in the choice of field bean varieties are straw height, earliness of ripening, disease resistance and yield. As in other organic crops, yield is influenced more by growing conditions than by variety and organic growers should select for agronomic characteristics before yield. Earliness of ripening is more important in beans than in many other crops. Late maturing varieties are harvested in cooler weather when drying of the crop in the field is slow.

Normally beans stand well, and although brackling (bending of the rachis) may occur it is unlikely to result in seed loss. Pod splitting and bird damage only occur if harvest is delayed considerably. On heavy soils, late maturing varieties increase the chance of damage to soil structure from heavy harvesting machinery as soils become wet in autumn.

Tall varieties compete better with weeds than short varieties. Although early crop vigour is the most important feature in competition with weeds, final height gives an indication of competitive ability. The recommended lists of field bean varieties suggest an inverse relationship between final straw height and earliness in beans, which may be because of the indeterminate growth habit, so variety choice is a compromise. If harvested in good condition, bean straw can be baled and used for bedding or feed, and has a higher feed value than wheat straw (Knott *et al.*, 1994).

Diseases of field beans include chocolate spot (*Botrytis fabae* and *B.cinerea*), downy mildew (*Peronospora viciae*) and *Ascochyta* leaf and pod spot (*Ascochyta fabae*). The most likely of these to trouble organic crops is chocolate spot, which cannot be controlled by rotation. Chocolate spot is influenced by season and location and affects winter beans more than spring beans. Comparative data for this disease is not available, though casual observations suggest that there are differences between varieties. Downy mildew should not be a problem where a good rotation is practiced and resistant varieties are used. *Ascochyta* is controlled through seed health standards.

Varieties of combining peas can be grouped by seed and flower colour, leaf type and sowing time. The majority of combining peas are spring-sown. Coloured-flowered varieties are grown for forage and produce brown seeds with a specialised market for pigeon feed. Almost all modern pea varieties are semi-leafless and, compared to normal-leaved peas, have larger stipules and the leaflets replaced by tendrils so that plants bind together more. Semi-leafless peas may be less competitive with weeds than normal-leaved peas (Greven, 2000). Seed colour and type determine the end use. Marrowfats and some blue peas are suitable for human consumption, large blues can be used in pet foods after micronising (treatment with infrared radiation to improve digestibility), and white-seeded peas are mostly used in animal feed compounding.

Factors in varietal choice for combining peas include seed colour, straw length, earliness of ripening and disease resistance. Peas frequently lodge severely before harvest so resistance to lodging and ease of combining are also important; semi-leafless varieties lodge later and less completely than normal-leaved varieties. This has implications for how fast the crop dries in the field, how readily weeds grow through the lodged crop and how easily the crop can be combined. Straw height is not necessarily associated with susceptibility to lodging, and analysis of SAC data indicates a positive correlation between straw strength and plant height (unpublished data). Tall varieties such as Eiffel and Nitouche compete more effectively with weeds than shorter ones such as Elan or Croma.

The main diseases for growers of organic combining peas to consider are downy mildew (*Peronospora viciae*), leaf and pod spots (*Ascochyta pisi*,

Mycosphaerella pinoides and *Phoma medicaginis*), botrytis (*Botrytis cinerea*), and pea bacterial blight (*Pseudomonas syringae*). Downy mildew is potentially a serious disease of pea crops. It is soil borne and may be avoided by rotations which allow four years between pea crops and by using resistant varieties. Botrytis affects peas after flowering, and is most serious in humid weather. There is evidence from Scottish trials of small varietal differences in resistance to botrytis (SAC, 2000).

Table 2.5.   Examples of pulse varieties for organic rotations

Crop	Region	Variety	Characteristics
Winter beans	England	Clipper	Tall straw, good disease resistance and high yield. Later than some varieties so unlikely to suit northern areas. Coloured flowers.
Spring beans	England	Lobo	Fairly tall, strong straw and earlier-than-average maturity, but below average resistance to disease. Coloured flowers.
Spring beans	Scotland	Victor	Early maturity, shorter-than-average but stiff straw. Average yield. Weak on downy mildew. Coloured flowers.
Spring peas	England	Nitouche	Tall, strong straw with good ease of combining. Average maturity. Good yield in conventional trials and good resistance to downy mildew. Large blue seed.
Spring peas	Scotland	Eiffel	Early. Tall, stiff straw with good ease of combining. Below average yield in conventional trials and risk of downy mildew. White seed.

Date of ripening in peas is important in northern areas. Differences in maturity of a few days in the south are multiplied three or four times in the north. Only relatively early varieties of combining peas are recommended in Scotland. Delays in harvest under organic conditions, especially where weeds are not completely eliminated, can lead to slow combining, damage to machinery, and a wet, discoloured sample, with a high admixture.

Yields from lupin variety trials can be found in NIAB (2000b). In NIAB trials, winter varieties were harvested later than spring varieties, were taller and higher yielding. For both spring and winter lupins tall varieties with early maturity are to be preferred in organic rotations. Some spring varieties are very short and therefore unsuitable for organic production.

In the absence of organically-managed trials on pulse crops, selections for organic rotations have to be based on data from non-organic trials. Some varietal selections are given in Table 2.5. Once again, growers may not consider the criteria used in selecting these to be appropriate for their own situations and should base their selections on their own criteria.

ORGANICALLY GROWN SEED

UKROFS, and hence all UK certification bodies, requires that growers have a derogation before purchasing and planting seed of non-organic origin. The commercial production of organically-grown seed is in its infancy and the range of varieties available is currently limited, therefore to secure the most appropriate cultivars it is essential to order early.

There is some scope for certification bodies to give derogations where organically-grown varieties are available, but not ideally suited to the end use or growing situation. However it is possible that growers may have to grow less than ideal cultivars to retain certification. Home-saved seed is an alternative option but there are issues of seed-borne diseases and weed seed spread to consider and these are discussed elsewhere in this publication (Chapter 7).

REFERENCES

Acamovic, T. (2001). Feeding peas and lupins to poultry. *Pea and Bean Progress*, Summer 2001.

Anon (2001). *New Lupins*. Goreham and Bateson Agriculture, Downham Market, UK.

Barrington L., Stocker P., Haward R. and Yeats B. (2001). Eye on the market. *Organic Farming*, 70, 10.

Biddle, A.J., Knott, C.M., and Gent, G.P. (1988). *Pea Growing Handbook*. Processors and Growers Research Organisation, Peterborough.

Bulson, H. (1993). Spring beans: low tannin varieties. *Elm Farm Research Centre Bulletin*, 5, 10.

Bulson, H.A.J., Snaydon, R.W. and Stopes, C.E. (1997) Effects of plant density on intercropped wheat and field beans in an organic farming system. *J. agric. Sci., Cambs*, 128, 59-71.

Cormack, W.F. (1997). Testing the sustainability of a stockless arable rotation on a fertile soil in Eastern England. In *Resource Use in Organic Farming* (eds J. Isart and J.J. Llerena), Proceedings of the 3rd ENOF Workshop, Ancona 4-6 June 1997. pp.127-135.

Ewing, W.N. (1997). *Feeds Directory*. Context, Heather, UK.

Fenwick, R. (2000).Cereals on trial. *Organic Farming*, 68, 16-18.

Fisher, N.M. (1996). The potential of grain and forage legumes in mixed farming systems. In *Legumes in Sustainable Farming Systems* (ed. D. Younie),. Occasional Symposium No.30, British Grassland Society, Aberdeen 2-4 September 1996. pp.290-299.

Greven, K. (2000). Competitive ability of pea (*Pisum sativum* L.) cultivars against weeds. Proceedings of the 13th International IFOAM Scientific Conference, 28-31 August 2000, Basel (eds T. Alfoldi, W. Lockeretz and U. Niggli). p.179.

Impey, L. (2001). Early drilling of winter lupins pays dividends and cuts seed costs. *Arable Farming*, 21 July 2001.

Knott, C.M., Biddle, A.J. and McKeown, B.M. (1994). *Field Bean Handbook*. Processors and Growers Research Organisation, Peterborough.

Lampkin, N. and Measures, M. (2001). *2001 Organic Farm Management Handbook*. University of Wales, Aberystwyth, and Elm Farm Research Centre, Newbury.

27

NIAB (2000a). *Cereal Variety Handbook*. National Institute of Agricultural Botany, Cambridge.

NIAB (2000b). *Pulse Variety Handbook*. National Institute of Agricultural Botany, Cambridge.

Rasmussen, I.A., Akegaard, M. and Olesen, J.E. (2000). Weed control in organic crop rotation experiments for grain production. Proceedings of the 13th International IFOAM Scientific Conference, 28-31 August 2000, Basel (eds T. Alfoldi, W. Lockeretz and U. Niggli). p.182.

SAC (2000). *Combining Peas 2001*. Scottish Agricultural College, Edinburgh.

Shield, I.F., Scott, T., Stevenson, H.J., Leach, J.E. and Todd, A.D. (2000). The causes of over-winter plant losses of autumn-sown white lupins (*Lupinus albus*) in different regions of the UK over three years. *J. agric. Sci., Cambs.*, 135 173-183.

Soil Association (2001). *The Organic Food and Farming Report 2000*. The Soil Association, Bristol.

Taylor, B.R., Richards, M.C., Mackay, J.M. and Cooper, J. (1991). Plant densities for combining peas in Scotland. In *Production and Protection of Legumes* (ed. R.J. Froud-Wiliams, P. Gladders, M.C. Heath, J.F.Jenkyn, C.M. Knott, A. Lane and D. Pink), *Aspects of Applied Biology*, 27, 309-312.

Taylor, B.R., Watson, C.W., Stockdale,E.A., McKinlay, R.G., Younie, D. and Cranstoun, D.A.S. (2001). *Current practices and Future Prospects for Organic Cereal Production: Survey and Literature Review*. Research Review No. 45, HGCA, London.

Watson, C.A., Fowler, S.M. and Wilman, D. (1993). Soil inorganic-N and nitrate leaching on organic farms. *Journal of Agricultural Science* 120, 361-369.

Welsh, J.,Wolfe, M. and Morris, M. (2001). Cereal Trials. *Organic Farming*, 69, 14-15.

Chapter 3

Species and Varietal Mixtures

M. S. WOLFE

Elm Farm Research Centre, Wakelyns Farm, Fressingfield, Suffolk IP21 5SD

INTRODUCTION

The major thrust in the development of non-organic agriculture has been the development of monoculture, largely to simplify production and processing systems. This has progressed mainly at the species level (wheat, rice, maize, potatoes and their numerous derivatives form the vast bulk of human food), but also at the variety level. Within each of the major species, only a handful of varieties dominates at any one time. It is also evident at the level of particular resistance genes. Many varieties have the same disease resistance; Bt maize and soya varieties are grown very widely in some countries. To develop successfully such wide use of monoculture requires close control of the production environment, largely through the use of soluble fertilisers, synthetic pesticides and growth regulators. This approach, however, while attempting to eliminate the negative aspects of the biological environment through the control of pests, diseases, weeds and variations in soil fertility, also tends to eliminate the positive biological processes that can buffer crops against all of these factors.

At the other extreme, natural plant communities usually comprise a range of species, varieties or gene combinations. The community and its components are never constant; they vary in composition and frequency both within and between seasons. The diversity and dynamism of the community is driven by environmental variation, both physical (climate and weather) and biological (pests, parasites, competition). The nature of the diversity buffers the community against environmental variation and restricts development of pests and pathogens. Such communities are characterised by a wide range of elements of biodiversity, all of which interact to provide some function in the dynamics of the community.

A particularly important feature of natural communities, additional to the fact that they are not dependent on any external inputs except light, air and water (indeed, contamination by external synthetic inputs can lead to their destruction), is that they are highly productive (Tilman, 1997). Reich *et al.* (2001) have shown recently that experimental communities of 16 species, at 11.43 t/ha, produced 55% more biomass than the mean of the component species grown in monocultures (7.35 t/ha). With enhanced CO_2 and N_2 application, as expected from global climate change and human population increase, the 16-species mixture increased by 35% to 15.43 t/ha whereas the monoculture biomass increased by only 17% to 8.6 t/ha. In other words, not only was the complex mixture more productive, it was better able to respond to the major forecast changes in the environment.

Modern organic agriculture, which may also be described as ecological agriculture, is concerned with understanding and managing naturally occurring processes and organisms so as to minimise or eliminate the use of external inputs other than light, air and water. A major objective is to focus on aspects of functional biodiversity in the natural environment that provide the tools essential for agricultural production. Familiar examples are the use of legume crops for their nitrogen fixation, encouraging mycorrhizal relationships in roots and soil for phosphorus availability, encouraging beneficial insects as predators of pests and the use of plant host resistances to different diseases. There are many other examples and, no doubt, many that are as yet unknown or unappreciated. For this reason, it is important to encourage as wide a range as possible of different elements and their potential interactions in organic agriculture systems. In this sense, the advantages of crop rotation are well-recognised in organic agriculture and form the basis of certification systems. However, there is a crucial need to develop much further in terms of the application of biodiversity, to increase productivity while minimising external inputs.

INTER-CROPPING FOR DIVERSITY

The objective of the organic farmer is to build up the range of positive biological processes in such a way as to achieve high levels of output without the direct and indirect costs of external inputs. Logically, therefore, the organic farmer has to develop towards polyculture rather than monoculture, at least to the levels of complexity that will deliver appropriate levels of biological inputs while maintaining a workable system. Finckh and Wolfe (1998) proposed a simple classification of polycultural approaches based on the use of a range of different species over time on a single management unit:

A. **Sole (single) cropping**: different crops are used but are managed singly. This includes:
-   **Rotational cropping**, which involves production of different crops among fields and over years.
-   **Sequential cropping**, involving two or more crops in sequence in the same field in one year.

B. **Inter-cropping**: two or more crops are managed simultaneously in the same field. The degree of interaction among the crops depends on their arrangement:
-   **Mixed inter-cropping**: maximum interspersion to maximise interactions (includes variety mixtures at the variety level).
-   **Row inter-cropping**: crops are planted in alternating rows to simplify management; interactions are reduced.
-   **Strip inter-cropping**: two or more crops are grown in strips that are wide enough for independent management but narrow enough to maintain some interactions among the crops.
-   **Plot inter-cropping**: the field is divided into plots or blocks which contain different single species; interactions may be limited.

Relay inter-cropping is a further system in which, for example, the strips in a strip inter-crop may be replaced at different times by other crops.

Most importantly, various forms of polyculture can be combined. For example, a rotation may consist of different strip inter-crops in which the crops themselves are grown as variety mixtures. Different levels of polyculture may be appropriate for different functions. For example, it is recognised that maximal restriction of diseases caused by air-borne plant pathogens can only be obtained by intimate variety mixing. On the other hand, some weeds and soil-borne diseases can be restrained by simple crop rotation. Thus the complexity of a system will depend on the highest common denominator. For example, if air-borne plant diseases are a major limiting factor in one area, then it may be necessary to concentrate on the use of both variety and species mixtures. Under less epidemic pressure, simpler inter-cropping systems may be adequate.

To review all forms of polycultural system would require a book rather than a chapter. This chapter concentrates therefore on species and variety mixtures, with particular emphasis on the use of variety mixtures for disease restriction since this approach is supported by a comprehensive literature.

HOW MIXTURES WORK

Mixtures of varieties or species can operate in many different ways to provide environmental buffering or restriction of diseases, pests or weeds (see review by Finckh and Wolfe, 1998). Because of the greater physical and genetical differences among species than among varieties, it is likely that species mixtures will tend to exhibit larger mixture effects. Some of the main mechanisms can be summarised:

A. Mixtures and environmental buffering:

a. Sread of genetic variation – different components have different potentials.

b. Complementation – the actions of different components may be complementary.
c. Niche differentiation – different components occupy more or less different niches within the overall environment.

B. Mixtures and disease restriction:

a. Increased distance between susceptible plants (main effect).
b. Non-susceptible plants act as barriers against spore dispersal.
c. Pathogens non-virulent on one variety may induce resistance against otherwise virulent races.
d. Selection for most resistant and/or competitive host genotypes.
e. Interactions among pathogen strains on host plants (reviewed by Finckh and Wolfe, 1998; Garrett and Mundt, 1999).

C. Mixtures and insect pests:

a. Reduction of density of individual hosts.
b. Reduction of visual or olfactory cues for insects.
c. Enhancement of natural enemies.
d. Alteration of host quality (with respect to the insect pest) through plant-plant interactions (reviewed by Andow, 1991).

D. Mixtures and weeds:

a. Increased plant density leads to reduction of bare soil and increases competition for light, water and nutrients
b. Layering of crop components increases competition for light, water and nutrients
c. Diversity of tillage needs and operations may disturb weeds reviewed by Liebmann and Dyck (1993) and Liebmann (1995).

In addition, the effects of selection among different hosts in a mixture may mean that a variety that is less competitive than the others, for whatever reason, may use less space, light, water and nutrients than its neighbours – which may then use those surplus resources. Such **compensation** is uncommon in monocultures where

33

all plants are, potentially, equally competitive. This is partly why mixtures may have more stable yields than monocultures over different environments (see below).

MIXTURES AND DISEASE

During the late 1970s in the UK, there was an initially rapid commercialisation of variety mixtures, particularly in wheat and barley. Unfortunately, as the acreage expanded, mixtures were discouraged increasingly by maltsters and millers who did not want to buy mixed grain, despite the possibility that the components might have complementary quality characteristics.

Nevertheless, by 1981, wheat mixture development was sufficiently effective for Mr Gordon Rennie to gain the world record wheat yield at the time (13.99 t/ha) with a mixture grown in Scotland (Newton and Swanston, 1999). Iinterest in the use of mixtures for restricting mildew on barley spread to the former German Democratic Republic where, during the 1980s, the whole spring barley acreage was eventually sown to a range of mixtures. This strategy led to an 80% reduction in the national mildew level with a consequent massive saving in fungicide use (Wolfe, 1992). The mixtures used commercially were put together by agreement among breeders, pathologists and maltsters, thus ensuring that high malt quality for export was maintained during the period of mixture cultivation.

The extensive literature, particularly on variety mixtures and disease restriction, has been reviewed recently from different perspectives (Wolfe and Finckh, 1997; Finckh and Wolfe, 1997, 1998, Finckh *et al.*, 2000). The general conclusion from field plot experiments is that mixtures of varieties differing in their resistance to a disease will sustain a level of disease similar to that of the most resistant of the components. If the disease level is sufficient to limit yield, then the mixture will tend to have a level of yield greater than the mean of the component varieties grown alone and often greater than that of the highest yielding component.

For illustration, Table 3.1 summarises a body of yield data obtained for barley with powdery mildew infection during the 1970s and 1980s. Many different three-component mixtures were used in the trials, but the mixtures were consistently about the best both for disease level and for yield. From the trial results it was abundantly clear at the time that the relative performance of the individual varieties could not be predicted at the beginning of each trial. The best strategy from a practical point-of-view in terms of minimising infection and maximising yield was, therefore, to grow the mixture rather than a single selected component or all three components.

Table 3.1. **Summary of yield (t/ha) comparisons for field trials in England over 11 years comparing the yields of different mixtures of three varieties of barley with their components grown as pure stands.**

a. **Mean yields**

No. of trial comparisons	Mean yield of mixtures	Mean yield of components	% increase (P<0.001)
122	5.61	5.20	7.88

b. **Ranking summary**

Number of times mixture yielded more than only:			
0 components	1 component	2 components	All 3
0	12	50	60

The mixture advantage was due largely to restriction of powdery mildew because resistance was effective and infection was consistently severe (data from Wolfe, 1987).

In one subset of the data using four popular varieties, the four possible 3-variety permutations were grown as mixtures in each of eight consecutive seasons during the 1980s (Wolfe, 1991). At the end of the period, the trial was repeated in Switzerland. Overall, the mixtures reduced mildew infection by almost half and gave an average yield increase of 10%, relative to the means of the component varieties grown alone. Importantly, over the whole period, each mixture combination yielded more than the highest yielding component.

WIDER ASPECTS OF DISEASE RESTRICTION IN MIXTURES

Host crops for which variety mixtures have proven to be effective in terms of disease restriction now include both annuals (wheat, barley, oats, triticale, maize, rice, soya bean and other bean species, lettuce, potato, oilseed rape, swede) and perennials (coffee, willow, apple). So far, there appears to be only one crop for which mixtures have proved to be ineffective, namely cassava (Daellenbach, pers. comm.).

However, the example data given in Table 3.1 and in many other publications focus on a single disease of a particular crop, normally regarded as the single most important disease in the trials in question. In practice, farmers will also be concerned about other diseases. The mechanisms by which a mixture restricts disease, summarised above, suggest that a variety mixture should be effective in restricting epidemic development of a wide range of air-borne pathogens. This has been shown to be so, with clear evidence for restriction of powdery mildews, rust diseases, *Septorias*, *Rhynchosporium* and others. Perhaps more importantly, it is clear that simultaneous restriction of several diseases can occur in practice (Wolfe, 1993) as was found in the trial noted in Table 3.2. Here, in addition to the large restriction in leaf rust development on the mixture, both powdery mildew and *Septoria tritici* were restricted on the same mixture to levels close to those of the more resistant component varieties.

Again, from the disease restriction mechanisms noted above, it would appear that host mixtures would be effective only against air-borne plant pathogens. However, Vilich-Meller (1992,1993) has demonstrated that both species and variety mixtures of cereals can restrict the development of major soil-borne diseases. It seems that the main mechanism involves the interaction of cereal allelochemicals (e.g. cyclic hydroxamic acids) with the pathogens.

Other soil-borne allelopathic interactions between species (though not with mixtures) have been noted by Kirkegaard *et al.* (1998) and Smith *et al.* (1999) who demonstrated the importance of brassica roots and crop residues in limiting the development of, for example, take all in wheat. This provides, potentially, an interesting pathological reason for the common production of wheat/mustard mixtures in India.

MIXTURE EFFECTS AND THEIR INTERACTIONS

In many mixtures, we can expect to see a range of different effects simultaneously. For example, Bulson *et al.* (1990) reported on the advantages of wheat/bean mixtures in suppressing weeds. Prior work on this system by the author also showed that such mixtures could reduce relative infestation by black bean aphid. Similarly, in cereal trials carried out by Elm Farm Research Centre (www.efrc.com), some species and variety mixtures showed simultaneous restriction of both weed infestation and disease spread.

There may also be a direct interaction between effects on weeds and disease. For example, in the same EFRC trial in 2000 (Table 3.2), for observations made in late July, weed infestation in the winter wheat variety Claire and in the mixture of the three varieties Claire, Consort and Riband, was considerably less than in the other two mixture components, Consort and Riband. At the same time, the levels of leaf rust (the worst of the leaf diseases on all varieties) on Claire and on the mixture were considerably less than on Consort and Riband. This suggests that plants heavily infected with disease are less well able to resist weed infestation than those that are less infected.

The opposite interpretation might also be true, that a heavier weed infestation may predispose plants to greater disease susceptibility, though one might expect a larger weed population to interfere with spore dispersal.

Other interactions should be expected, for example, where different components have different but positive effects in relation to soil nutrients. If the whole plant community is affected, we might then expect to find some influence on disease or pest interactions.

Table 3.2. **Leaf rust (% leaf cover), weeds (% ground cover) and yield (t/ha) of three wheat varieties grown as sole plots or the three variety mixture in Suffolk in 2000** (EFRC trial).

Variety	Leaf rust (%)	Weed cover (%)	Yield (t/ha)
Claire	2.5	25	5.33
Consort	46.3	45	2.54
Riband	22.5	45	2.76
Mean	23.8	38	3.54
Mixture	7.5	30	4.1
% mix/mean	31.6	78	115.7

Yield effect significant at P<0.05

YIELD STABILITY OF MIXTURES

Reliable and thus stable yield is of major interest for growers. To assess the yield stability of mixtures and pure stands, data from Polish trials were analysed using regression analysis as modified by Mundt *et al.* (1995). Here, an example is given for a trial with seven barley cultivars in pure stands and the 35 possible three-way mixtures grown in seven different environments in Poland (Table 3.3).

The yields of all of the pure stands and mixtures in the trial were ranked and regressed on the mean yield of the environments in which the experiment was conducted. A high mean rank with low mean square error (MSE) and a non-significant, or at least positive slope is the most desirable combination. While the ranks of the mixtures, with one exception, did not range below 10, the ranks of the pure stands ranged over a much larger amplitude. The MSE of the mixtures were overall much lower than for the pure stands.

Table 3.3. **Yield, powdery mildew severity and the yield stability of barley cultivar mixtures relative to their pure stands in five experiments (each with 6 to 11 repetitions) conducted between 1987 and 1995 in Poland.**

Cereal	CV[1]	Year	Environ -ments	Rel. yield	Rel. disease	Rel. MSE[2]
Spring Barley (f)[a]	7	87-89	7	1.03	0.81	0.56
Spring Barley (m)	6	88-89	6	1.03	0.85	0.48
Spring Barley (f)	5	91-93	11	1.02	0.70	0.79
Spring Barley (m)	4	91-93	11	1.02	0.60	0.67
Winter Barley (f)	5	93-95	10	1.02	-	0.97
Spring Barley (f)	6	94-96	9	1.01	0.77	0.82
Spring Barley (m)	4	94-96	9	0.99	0.74	0.52
Spring Barley (f)	5	94-96	9	1.01	0.68	1.07

[a] f=Feed barley, m=Malting barley
[1] CV = Coefficient of variation
[2] MSE = Mean square error

Such results are encouraging although, in this set of trials, the apparent yield advantage of the mixtures appeared small. It is likely that the scale of the effects recorded was a reflection of the frequent problem of the need to extrapolate data from small plot trials to the outcome of using mixtures on a large scale. Indeed, we may expect positive mixture effects to increase as the scale of production increases, simply because the opportunity for interference from external sources of pathogen spores decreases with increasing scale.

Three-way mixtures and pure stands of four to seven cultivars were compared and ranked within each environment. Ranks were regressed on the mean yield per environment. The mean square error (MSE) of the rank regression of mixtures is expressed relative to the MSE of the rank regression of pure stands. A relative MSE less than 1 indicates higher yield stability for the mixture than the pure stands (data from Finckh *et al.*, 1997).

MIXTURES ON THE GRAND SCALE

To illustrate the factor of scale of mixture area on disease level, collaboration between Oregon State University, the International Rice Research Institute (IRRI) and Chinese scientists, led to a remarkable experiment on a grand scale. The researchers stimulated a unique co-operation in Yunnan Province, China whereby all rice fields in five townships in 1998 (812 ha) and in 10 townships in 1999 (3,342 ha) were planted to rice mixtures. The objective was to restrict blast disease on certain susceptible rice varieties, which, as monocultures, would receive 3 to 8 fungicide applications to keep them free from disease. However, blast was 94% less severe when these varieties were planted in mixtures with resistant varieties, and fungicidal sprays were eliminated.

This spectacular reduction in blast was constant over the whole area in both seasons and was correlated with a considerable increase in yield relative to the components grown in monoculture. Even the resistant varieties, slightly infected in the first year, were more resistant in the second, because of the 'damping' effect of the mixtures over the larger test area. This may have been an effect of the relatively complex pathogen populations growing on the crop mixtures causing widespread induced resistance. The small and complex populations of the pathogen surviving from one crop to the next could also have been less well-adapted to the variety mixtures than would pathogen populations surviving on one monoculture variety between seasons.

SPECIES MIXTURES

In the past, before the widespread use of herbicides, insecticides and fungicides, species mixtures were the rule rather than the exception, based on clear advantages in performance such as in yield and weed control. Because of the relatively limited use of species mixtures in modern agriculture, research to uncover the less obvious benefits of particular mixtures has been slow to unfold. For example, in the 13th and 14th Centuries, the use of mixed cereal species was already well established as a means of maintaining stability of crop production – albeit at a low (0.5 t/ha) level. Oats mixed with vetch was commonly used for smothering weeds. However, nothing was known of the allelopathic effects of oats on weeds or on its ability, for example, to reduce *Fusarium* and other foot diseases of cereals either when intercropped or used as a pre-crop (Vilich-Meller, 1992). While allelopathic effects and disease suppression are often observed in the genus *Avena,* these effects are species and even cultivar specific and interactions with fertility management have been reported (Elmer and LaMondia, 1999).

The value of the centuries-old use of barley/oat mixtures has been confirmed in modern trials, showing that barley/oat mixtures always yielded as much or more than either component. An impressive example of modern production is in Poland, where, since the 1950s, official advice and encouragement was to grow only pure stands. Despite this advice, many growers chose to grow mixtures of cereals (barley-wheat, barley-oat) or cereals with legumes and the area under species mixtures increased from 400,000ha in 1970 to 1.2 m. ha in 1993 (Czembor and Gacek, 1996). The main reason appears to have been the advantage of stability. In a similar way, hundreds of thousands of hectares of barley/oat mixtures are also grown currently in Ontario.

Following the relatively recent widespread use of clovers in Europe and elsewhere, farmers quickly realised the advantages of clover-grass mixtures in terms of productivity and stability and such mixtures are now the best-known form of species mixture in temperate climates. There are, however, very many more possibilities among crops for off-farm sales, animal feed and cover or catch cropping. Many include mixtures of different gramineous and leguminous species (grass/clover variations, wheat or oats with beans, barley/peas, maize/beans, grazing rye/vetch, oats/vetch, cereal/clover bi-cropping etc.). However, many other actual and potential combinations are possible, stimulated either by past experience or by unfolding information, for example, concerning the value of Brassica crops in terms of root exudates helping in disease resistance or weed control.

The organic farmer, in particular, also needs to be increasingly aware of the potential for improving the efficiency of plant nutrition by exploiting interactions among the species that encourage mycorrhizal associations (*Gramineae, Leguminosae*), nitrogen fixation (*Leguminosae*) and K release (*Chenopodiaceae*).

QUALITY ASPECTS

An obvious end-use of species and variety mixtures is as animal feed (with cereals either as whole crop silage or grain) or for cover for catch crops; the final mixture may or may not need separation back into its components. For home feed use, species and quality will determine the initial composition of the mixture. For example, winter barley variety mixtures are grown in Scotland as a 6-row high yielding feed quality variety mixed with a 2-row to increase specific weight, i.e. to increase quality (Newton and Swanston, 1999).

For off-farm use, there is no doubt that the uptake of cereal variety mixtures has been limited by the uncertainty among growers of their ability to sell their grain, particularly to industrial end-users who are concerned about specific varieties. In the north-western USA, varieties within the same market class are not segregated at the elevator. Thus, it makes no difference for grain customers if varieties are grown in pure stand or in mixture. However, in Europe, where the focus will probably remain on variety rather than on category of grain, methods such as the use of molecular markers may provide practical help to ensure that mixture composition is close to a required specification.

In general, there is probably more variability in end-product quality among grain from different fields of the same variety than there is among crops of the same varieties grown together in the same fields. If so, marketing of grain from variety mixtures need not be an issue. For example, Baumer and Wybranietz (1995) compared the variability in malting quality of pure stands and variety mixtures of malting barley varieties that belonged to the same quality class over eight locations. They found that the variability in quality due to location effects was significantly higher for the pure stands than for the mixtures. More recent trials confirmed these findings (Newton *et al.*, 1998): growing both winter and spring barley cultivars in combinations of different malting quality did not affect malting quality significantly except for decreases in homogeneity of cell wall modification. A particular mixture of three winter malting cultivars even gave higher hot water extracts than the component cultivars in pure stands, with no adverse effects on homogeneity (Newton *et al.*, 1998). An important aspect of final quality is the interaction between nutrient supply and grain quality. Under organic conditions, for example, varieties with lower molecular weight gluten often have better quality than the high molecular weight gluten varieties that are bred for high input agricultural systems (G. Völkel, personal communication).

For the separation of mixture components that are obviously different, then mechanical or optical methods may be appropriate. For example, we have a current interest in developing the use of mixtures of potato varieties to slow down the development of blight epidemics. If this were to prove successful, then there are already optical character recognition methods available to help in separating the components at harvest should this prove to be necessary.

DISCUSSION

Production of mixtures

Historical data, research and practical experience all point strongly to the multiple benefits of biodiverse agricultural systems. However, despite the accumulated knowledge, there is still much to be learnt in terms of determining the best ways of obtaining appropriate levels of diversity to ensure the sustainability of different systems. For example, there are many ways of achieving diversity in cropping systems, though currently, organic agriculture often uses little more than crop rotation based on a limited number of crop species and varieties. One constraint is the limited range of varieties of some species that are currently available. This constraint is inevitable over the next few years partly because of the limited size of the organic sector and partly because of the switchover period towards the use of only organically raised seed for certified organic production.

There are two ways of dealing with this problem on farm. The first is to produce one's own seed if it are not available from organic sources (Cherfas *et al.*, 1996). The second, if practicable, is to grow a seed crop of the intended mixture so as to limit the scale of separate seed purchases and of the amount of seed mixing needed.

The potential problem with growing mixtures for seed, however, is the possibility that there may be a shift in composition of the mixture during seed production. For example, Wolfe (1991) found that in a series of spring barley mixtures sown initially with equal weights of three components, the variety Egmont tended to dominate in the harvested mixed grain. After only one cycle, almost half of the seed was of Egmont in each of three mixtures. By the end of a third cycle, almost 90% of the seed was Egmont in each mixture. In one sense, some shift in composition might be regarded as an advantage, indicating that the mixture was adjusting to local conditions. In this particular example, however, the shift was almost certainly due to the consistent vigour of Egmont seedlings relative to the other varieties. It should be possible to limit the effects of this problem by checking the relative vigour of the seedlings of the components and by limiting seed production cycles to one, or two at most.

Virtually all species and varieties are bred and selected for performance in pure stands, which may limit their potential in mixtures. This is unlikely to change because of the wide and extending range of possible mixtures in which individual species or varieties may be involved. Rather than attempt to test the mixing ability of a variety with all possible other varieties and species with which it might be grown, it would be more practical to select for specific characters useful in mixture production such as early seedling vigour or complementary quality factors.

Breeding for diversity

To breed varieties and species specifically for use in mixtures would be extremely difficult in practice, not least because of the wide range of mixtures in which a particular species or variety might feature. A possible way round this problem is to develop methods of population breeding. This would follow the notion of evolutionary plant breeding (Suneson, 1956), to produce composite crosses involving a wide range of desirable parent lines and varieties. The composite cross would then be grown at different sites and subject to local selection. Earlier experiments in this direction (Allard and Adams, 1969) led to the production of well-buffered, stable, high-yielding populations.

Mixtures and rotation

A major increase in the use of species and variety mixtures could lead to an important issue in relation to crop rotation. Current organic certification rules stipulate intervals of several years between production of certain species in the same area. This could raise some difficulties in relation to the use of some species as mixture components for specific purposes. One example could be the desirability of using, say, a mustard/vetch mixture as a cover crop between other crops to provide soil-borne disease control, weed smothering and nitrogen input. In the short-term, the answer to this question would be to extend the whole rotation so as to separate adequately the brassica used in the cover crop from any other brassica used as a production crop.

For the long-term, research is needed to determine whether or not the use of a series of complex species mixtures would be sufficiently effective in terms of soil-borne disease control so as to allow a relaxation of the rules concerning temporal separation of particular crops. Clearly, random plant displacement in such mixtures would at least ensure a limited probability of plants of one species growing in exactly the same position in the field in, say, alternate years.

Diversity at different levels

Following an effective crop rotation, the simplest step forward in increasing diversity and its effectiveness is to grow variety mixtures, followed by species mixtures. As pointed out earlier, it is important here to keep in mind the potential for exploitation of different levels of diversity simultaneously, e.g. in a rotation of species mixtures, each species is used as a variety mixture, and so on. At the most complex level, we need to consider further the role of agroforestry, integrating trees with crop and animal production (Wolfe, 1998).

One example under development is an agroforestry system involving trees with crop and chicken rotation. The potential interactions are many and complex. The trees, in the form of biodiverse hedges with standards, should provide a habitat for a wide range of organisms including, for example, many beneficial insects. They will also provide shelter and an attractive environment for the chickens and for a range of plants chosen to help in the nutrition and welfare of the chickens, which should in turn encourage nutrient recycling between the animals and trees. The nutrient cycling will then help subsequent crop development, and so on.

A key principle, as we expand through increasing levels of diversity, is to ensure that each level adds something further to help crop productivity, stability and sustainability. In other words, we should ensure that we make the best use of natural diversity to carry out as many essential processes of agricultural production as possible. This needs to be stressed most for the further development of organic agriculture but is equally relevant for other systems.

REFERENCES

Allard, R.W., Adams, J., (1969). Population studies in predominantly self-pollinating species XIII Intergenotypic competition and population structure in barley and wheat, *Amer. Nat.* 103, 620-645.

Baumer M., Wybranietz J., (1995). Einfluss von Sortenmischungen auf die Malzqualitaet der Sommergerste, in: Talk presented at the meeting of the working group on Saatgutwesen in Hannover, Germany, 17./ 18. March 1995.

Cherfas, J., Fanton, M. and Fanton, J. (1996). *The Seed Savers' Handbook.* Grover Books: Bristol, pp 168. ISBN 1 899233 01 6.

Czembor H.J., Gacek E.S., (1996). The use of cultivar and Species Mixtures to Control Diseases and for Yield Improvement in Cereals in Poland, in: E.Limpert, M.R.Finckh, M.S.Wolfe, (Eds.), *Proceedings of the 3rd Workshop on Integrated Control of Cereal Mildews across Europe*, Nov. 5-10 1994. Kappel a. Albis, Switzerland, Office for Official Publications of the EC, Brussels, Belgium, 177-184.

Elmer, W. H. and J. L. LaMondia. (1999). Influence of ammonium sulfate and rotation crops on strawberry black root rot. *Plant Dis.* **83**:119-123.

Finckh, M. R., Gacek, E. S., Goyeau, H., Lannou, C., Merz, U., Mundt, C. C., Munk, L., Nadziak, J., Newton, A. C., de Vallavieille-Pope, C. and Wolfe, M. S. (2000) Cereal variety and species mixtures in practice, with emphasis on disease resistance. *Agronomie* 20: 813-837.

Finckh M.R., Wolfe M.S., (1997). The use of biodiversity to restrict plant diseases and some consequences for farmers and society, in: L.E.Jackson, (Ed.), *Ecology in Agriculture*, Academic Press, San Diego, 199-233.

Finckh M.R., Wolfe M.S., (1998). Diversification strategies, in: D.G.Jones, (Ed.), *The Epidemiology of Plant Diseases*, Chapman and Hall, London, 231-259.

Garrett, K.A., Mundt, C.C., (1999). Epidemiology in mixed host populations. *Phytopathology* 89, 984-990.

Kirkegaard, J. A., M. Sarwar, P. T. W. Wong, and A. Mead. (1998). Biofumigation by brassicas reduces take-all infection, p. 465-468. In: *Proc. of the 9th Australian Agronomy Conference*, Wagga Wagga.

Kirkegaard, J. A. and M. Sarwar. (1999). Glucosinolate profiles of Australian canola (*Brassica napus annua* L.) and Indian mustard *(Brassica juncea* L.) cultivars: implications for biofumigation. *Aust.J.Agric.Res.* **50**:315-324.

Mundt C.C., Brophy L.S., Schmitt M.S., (1995). Disease severity and yield of pure-line wheat cultivars and mixtures in the presence of eyespot, yellow rust, and their combination, *Pl. Path.* 44, 173-182.

Newton A.C., Swanston J.S., Guy D.C., Ellis R.P., (1998). The effect of cultivar mixtures on malting quality in winter and spring barley, *J. Inst. Brew.*104, 41-45.

Newton AC, Swanston JS. (1999). Cereal variety mixtures reducing inputs and improving yield and quality - why isn't everybody growing them? *Scottish Crop Research Institute Annual Report for 1998/99*, 55-59.

Reich, P B, Knops, J, Tilman, D, Craine, J, Ellsworth, D, Tjoelker, M, Lee, T, Wedin, D, Naeem S, Bahauddin, D, Hendrey, G, Jose, S, Wrage, K, Goth J and Bengston, W. (2001) Plant diversity enhances ecosystem responses to elevated CO2 and nitrogen deposition. *Nature* 410, 809-812.

Smith, B. J., M. Sarwar, P. T. W. Wong, and J. A. Kirkegaard. 1999. Suppression of cereal pathogens by canola root tissues in soil, p. 1-5. In: *Proceedings 10th International Rapeseed Congress, Canberra* (CD Publication).

Suneson, C.A., (1956). An evolutionary plant breeding method,

Agron. J. 48, 188-191.

Tilman, D., Lehman, C. L. and Thomson, K. T. (1997) Plant diversity and ecosystem productivity: Theoretical considerations. *Proc. Natl. Acad. Sci. USA*. 94:1857-1861.

Vilich-Meller, V. (1992). Mixed cropping of cereals to suppress plant diseases and omit pesticide applications. *Biological Agriculture and Horticulture* 8, 299-308.

Vilich, V. (1993). Crop rotation with pure stands and mixtures of barley and wheat to control stem and root rot diseases. *Crop Prot.* 12, 373-379.

Wolfe, M S (1991) Recent developments in using variety mixtures to control powdery mildew of barley. *Proceedings of the second workshop on Integrated Control of Cereal Mildews: Virulence patterns and their change.* Ed. J H Joergensen Riso, Denmark, January 1990.

Wolfe, M.S., (1992). Maintaining the value of our varieties, in: L. Munk, (Ed.), *Barley Genetics VI, vol. 2.* Munksgaard International Publishers, Copenhagen, 1055-1067.

Wolfe, M. S. (1998). Combining trees and crops. *New Farmer and Grower* 58, 30-31.

Wolfe, M. S. (2000). Crop strength through diversity. *Nature* 406, 681-682.

Wolfe M.S., Finckh M.R., (1997). Diversity of host resistance within the crop: effects on host, pathogen and disease, in: H.Hartleb, R.Heitefuss, H.H.Hoppe, (Eds.), *Plant resistance to fungal diseases*, G. Fischer Verlag, Jena, 378-400.

Zhu Y., Chen H., Fan J., Wang Y., Li Y., Chen J., Fan J., Yang S., Hu L., Leung H., Mew T. W., Teng P. S., Wang Z. and Mundt C.C. (2000). Genetic diversity and disease control in rice. *Nature* 406 718-722.

Chapter 4

Rotations and Nutrient Management Strategies

L. PHILIPPS[1], S.K. HUXHAM[2], S.R. BRIGGS[3] and D.L. SPARKES[2]

[1]Elm Farm Research Centre, Hamstead Marshall, Newbury, Berkshire RG20 0HR
[2]School of Biosciences, University of Nottingham Sutton Bonnington Campus, Loughborough, Leicestershire LE12 5RD
[3]Abacus Organic Associates, Rowan House, 9Pinfold Close, South Luffenham, Oakham, Rutland LE15 8NE

INTRODUCTION

The challenge for all organic farmers is to produce sufficient quantities of high quality food within the constraints of EU regulation, EEC No 2092/91. These challenges are exacerbated when the farming system is predominately based on arable crop production. Organic arable farmers are faced with technical problems such as nitrogen management and weed control, both of which have a considerable effect on the economic viability of a rotation. The market for organic grain crops has never been stronger. However, many farmers are still reluctant to convert as they lack sufficient knowledge or confidence to develop appropriate rotations and nutrient management strategies, especially where farms operate all-arable enterprises.

Whilst there has been a 24 percent increase in the area of organically farmed arable land from 8,200ha in 1997 (Soil Association 1998) to 10,800ha in 2000 (Soil Association 2000), there has been a steady decline in the proportion devoted to organic arable production compared to that used for livestock production, which rose by 72 percent over the same period (Soil Association 2000). Combining an increased demand for grain for livestock feeds with an increased demand from the food processing sector, this has resulted in an under supply of domestic organic cereals and pulses and an increased reliance on imports. This increasing demand for organic cereals and pulses will be exacerbated when proposed changes to organic standards in 2005 will require organic livestock to be fed on 100 percent certified organic feed.

The majority of organic farming in the UK is on mixed or livestock units and predominantly in central and western areas, with arable-only farms, mainly located in the eastern regions, being reluctant to develop livestock farming systems. There are a number of reasons behind this. EU production subsidies continue to support arable system profitability, and many arable-only farms no longer have livestock management expertise, infrastructure or a willingness to re-introduce livestock enterprises. To contemplate organic conversion, these farms would therefore have to depend on an arable-only or all-arable organic farming system, either initially or permanently. The high level of specialisation associated with all-arable farms has limited UK development of organic agriculture, especially in the eastern counties.

The continuing reluctance of farmers to convert all-arable farms hinges on the limited range of information on appropriate rotations and nutrient management strategies for different farming systems and resource circumstances. Fragstein (1996) found that the proportion of all-arable farms in Germany varied between 20% and 50%. Similarly, David *et al.* (1996) and Stopes *et al.* (1996b) reported that the all-arable system is becoming increasingly important in organic farming systems in, respectively, France and the UK.

In the recent past, the development of organic farming has been made possible by livestock production developing in a closed mixed system (Baars, 1998). As a result, most organic farming systems in Europe are based on a rotation with a large proportion of fodder crops, in combination with animal production (NRA, 1992). It is not economically viable for an all-arable rotation to include a long ley phase to provide a balance between fertility building and exploitative arable crops. The absence of a ley phase may also lead to greater problems with weeds, pests, diseases, soil structure, organic matter and fertility. Instead, short-term leguminous green manures may be used to accumulate N for the subsequent arable phases of the rotation. Trials on the duration, species composition and management of leguminous green manures demonstrated that red clover, cut and mulched, could supply a considerable amount of N (Stopes *et al.*, 1996a).

Replicated plot trials demonstrated that all-arable systems were agronomically viable in the early 1990s (Stopes & Millington, 1992). Field scale trails also demonstrated the viability of such systems (Cormack, 1996, Stopes *et al.*, 1996, Philipps *et al.*, 1999). However, they are highly dependent on the use of set-aside to provide income during the fertility building phases of the rotation.

This paper addresses the potential of predominately arable systems, by addressing conversion strategies, nutrient management, rotation design and the wider economic implications.

ALL-ARABLE CONVERSION STRATEGIES.

Research at the University of Nottingham focuses on this critical conversion period in an all-arable system. Typically a two-year red-clover ryegrass green manure is sown, cut, and mulched regularly to improve soil structure and nitrogen status. This is a popular strategy, eligible for both set-aside and organic aid payments. This conversion strategy is successful at supporting subsequent crop rotation, but is dependent on subsidies to be economically viable. The availability and level of support payments is under the discretion of the national government and the European Commission (e.g. set-aside 10 to50% until 2006, but can change at any time), and the continuation of such payments should not be relied upon to sustain the profitability of organic farming.

Alternatives to the two-year red clover-ryegrass ley conversion are being tested in a fully replicated experiment on an unretentive sandy loam soil previously managed conventionally with a winter wheat, second wheat, barley, oilseed rape, set-aside rotation. The experiment began in September 1999 following the harvest of the second wheat. To explore fully the dynamics between maximising profits and building optimum soil nitrogen, a range of conversion cropping strategies that stretch the economic and agronomic limits of the conversion are being tested (Table 4.1). Factors considered in strategy design include the potential to increase soil nitrogen through nitrogen fixation; the potential to create revenue through the sale of crops; and the result of different management demands on the variable and fixed costs. Altering the proportions and species of green manuring and cash cropping in each strategy has done this.

In the third year winter wheat will be grown across the entire experimental area as a test crop, to assess the effect of the different strategies on yield and quality of the first organic harvest. As the wheat crop will be the first eligible for organic premiums, the yield will influence the overall profitability of each strategy.

Plant growth and development are being monitored in each conversion strategy, along with detailed assessments of the soil, in particular the flows of soil nutrients. The impact of conversion strategies on profit, risk, return-on-investment and cash-flow is being modeled using a linear programming technique, and this economic analysis will be carried out under current and future policy scenarios.

Profitability

In the Nottingham study linear programming will be used to find the most profitable conversion solution for a farm converting to organic production. The model uses data from the field experiment and applies it to a farm undergoing a staggered organic conversion.

Using estimated future crop yields, the first year results suggest that harvesting a seed crop from a red clover ley would potentially be the

Table 4.1. The conversion strategies are two-year cropping sequences, all followed by wheat in the third year. (u/s = undersown with red clover, * cut and mulched over growing season)

Strategy	Year 1 crop	Year 2 crop	Expected fertility-building	Variable costs	Fixed costs	Potential return in a free-market
1	red clover/ryegrass as green manure *	red clover/ryegrass as green manure *	high	low	low	low
2	vetch as green manure	vetch/rye as green manure	high	high	high	low
3	red clover (seed)	red clover/ryegrass as green manure *	medium	low	medium	high
4	spring wheat (u/s)	red clover as green manure *	medium	medium	medium	medium
5	spring wheat	winter beans	low	medium	high	high
6	spring oats	winter beans	low	medium	high	high
7	spring wheat (u/s)	spring barley/ spring pea	low	high	high	high

most profitable of the conversion strategies tested, due to good yield and high seed value, thus producing the highest gross margin. However, the production of clover seed is a high-risk strategy, with highly variable yields and associated income levels.

Changing prices and yields of organic crops, and the relative prices of organic and conventional crops will impact on the profitability of each strategy. Sensitivity analysis is used to test how far crop yields or organic premiums can fall before using a different conversion strategy becomes the most profitable option - strategy "robustness". A full economic assessment and comparison of strategies will only be possible after the third year wheat harvest.

ROTATIONS AND NUTRIENT STRATEGIES, INCLUDING ALL-ARABLE SYSTEMS

Rotation Design

There are many factors influencing rotation design. The presence of livestock enterprises and forage requirements, soil type, weed incidence, climate, topography etc. These can broadly be categorized as resource, fertility or enterprise factors and their influence varies from site to site (Table 4.2). During and immediately after conversion the impact of historical land use and soil borne pest or disease issues can limit choices of crops in the rotation. Once an operational organic system has been developed, the interaction between these factors determines an appropriate rotation and cropping sequence. This may vary at a farm level or even at a field or part field level.

The key to the success of any rotation is that it is tailored so as to be 'site specific'. For any given site, soil quality is one of the key determinants in crop and economic performance. On fertile silt soils, organic all-arable systems have the potential to out-perform similar non-organic all-arable rotations over a nine-year period (Cormack, 1999). In these situations the ratio of cash crop to fertility building can be high. On more marginal soils the ratio may have to be lower.

Table 4.2. Factors influencing rotation design

Resource	Fertility	Enterprise
Soil type and quality	Soil type and quality	Soil type and quality
Climate	Fertility management	Livestock requirements
Farm geography & biodiversity	Legumes	Balance of fertility & exploitation
Farm history / cropping	Green manures	Fertility building choices
Weed levels from historic use may limit viability	Compost / FYM	Pest / disease breaks
Farm management (farm / contract managed)	Supplementary inputs	Weed management
Infrastructure and skills		Autumn vs spring crops
Integration with other farm activities		Crop choices
Other crops grown in locality		
Location of markets		

Pest and disease pressure is often greatly reduced in organic systems as a result of the greater crop diversity and natural predators and reduced levels of crop stress. However, competitive pressure from weeds is more variable. Weed control is primarily achieved by using rotations that contain a ley or green manure phase where a fertility building green manure is repeatedly grazed or mulched. This prevents a build up of weeds and further seed shed. The selection of crop types and varieties that have vigorous growth characteristics, especially during their early development stages has been shown to help out-compete weeds (Younie & Taylor, 1995).

Grain crops such as oats and triticale, which develop rapidly, tiller vigorously and have a tall stature, are significantly more competitive against weeds than the majority of modern wheat varieties which have been bred as dwarf varieties (Welsh *et al.*, 2001). The sequence of crops in the rotation has an important influence on weed competition, as does a mixture of autumn and spring sown crops within the rotation which allows mechanical control strategies to be used on different weeds or the same weed at different development stages (Welsh, 1998).

Mechanical methods of control can be used which focus on the use of pre-drilling, pre-emergence and post-emergence mechanical weeding and/or cultivations during summer months. There are three principle methods for the mechanical control of weeds; uprooting, cutting and burial, which rely on exhausting the energy of the weed or desiccation to cause death and these should be used to best advantage during the 'critical weed free period' (Welsh *et al.*, 1999).

The most common method of mechanical weed control in grain crops is the spring tine or 'comb harrow'. Research has demonstrated that whilst being a useful tool in many circumstances the window of opportunity for use is limited, especially on heavy soils. Growing grain crops planted on wide rows of 20 to 25cm allows the use of inter-row weed control. This has a wider window of opportunity and achieves more consistent weed kill (Welsh, 1998b) without detriment to crop performance. Recent research developments have resulted in the production of automated "magic eye" guidance systems that make this system of weed control increasingly attractive, especially for organic farms operating on heavy soils.

In addition to weed control, the late weeding of grain crops can also increase the mineralization of soil N during the critical grain development stages via the disturbance of topsoil and oxidisation of soil organic matter. If matched to critical crop development stages this could be a useful management tool in improving grain protein contents in bread making cereals where protein contents are often low. More research is required in this area.

Other areas of current interest are the applicability of minimal cultivations to organic crop production systems. These have demonstrable benefits of limiting soil cultivations, reducing soil N losses and decreasing disturbance of soil microbial populations. Other options include the use of bi-cropping or intercropping systems to provide soil mineral N from a leguminous crop to the non-leguminous crop as it grows. Growing pulses and cereals is common practice for arable silage. It is a less common practice for the production of grain crops. Bulson *et al.* (1996) showed that intercropping field beans and wheat was technical and economically viable and that the yield of the combined crop outperformed crops grown as pure stands, with the benefit of reduced crop disease pressure for both of the intercrops used.

As outlined earlier, yield is a key component in profitability of organic crops. The current models used to produce organic grain crops rely heavily on a cyclic rotation whereby fertility is built up over a period of typically 1 to 3+ years and subsequently exploited with a sequence of cash grain crops. The crops placed first in the exploitative phase of the rotation are typically those where the highest yield and greatest profit is desired. Crops later in the sequence typically result in reduced performance and profitability.

Current systems are generally pre-occupied with above-ground production, with below ground biomass production and diversity taking second place or largely ignored. A mixture of diverse crop types below ground is as important if not more important than above ground. Different rooting characteristics influence soil structure, aeration, mineral availability and mobility, and microbial activity. Combining cash crops with different rooting systems in the rotation is a first step. This can be further enhanced by integrating different green manures to add to the diversity of below-ground production. Green manures are widely used in organic farming systems to reduce soil N losses, to out-compete weeds, improve soil structure and soil organic matter levels. The deep rooting systems of many green manures also have the benefit of drawing up minerals such as potassium and phosphate from deeper in the soil profile and relocating them to the rooting zone of grain crops.

Grain protein content is a limiting factor in the production of bread making cereals. Even when sequenced as the first cash crop after the fertility-building phase, soil N release occurs from the point where the preceding green manure or legume-based ley is disturbed and cultivated. This results in a flux of soil N at germination and emergence. To improve grain protein contents a flux of soil N release at grain development would be more appropriate. This would require the retention of soil N at establishment and the release of soil N later in the crop production cycle.

For winter cereals this may prove difficult. On heavier soils it is often impossible to cultivate and plant in the spring. This results in soil N being lost over the winter period via leaching. On land that can support spring sown crops, an option may be to cultivate in late summer/early autumn and establish a quick growing green manure such as mustard or forage rape, which could then be incorporated prior to cereal drilling in the spring.

Green manures planted between crops over the winter period are used to retain soil N and reduce leaching. When these green manures are subsequently incorporated, their decomposition stimulates microbial activity and soil N release, which is available to the following crop. The ratio of the amount of carbon to the amount of nitrogen in the green manure crop, or C: N ratio, influences the rate of decomposition of the green manure and nutrient availability. C: N ratios vary depending on the composition of different materials and their growth stages. Young green material with C: N ratios of 15 will break down rapidly and release N. Older more "woody" material with a C: N ratio of 80:1 will break down more slowly and release N over a longer period. Material with a high C: N ratio has a relatively low percentage of nitrogen and conversely a low C: N ratio has a relatively high percentage of nitrogen.

Well-mulched young green manure residues decompose slowly in the soil because they are relatively stable, having undergone a significant amount of decomposition already. Residues with C: N ratios in the mid 20s will make soil N readily available as they decompose. However mature plant residues with a C: N ratio of over 40:1 (Table 4.3) may cause temporary problems in the supply of N to plants as micro-organisms may immobilize surrounding soil N to aid their growth and reproduction thus diminishing the amount of nitrate and ammonium available for crop development.

Table 4.3.   Carbon:Nitrogen (C:N) ratios of some organic materials

Material	C: N ratio
Soil micro-organisms	7
Soil	10 – 12
Clover	13
Compost	15
Grazing rye	36
Maize stems	60
Wheat straw	80
Fresh sawdust	400

There is potential to use different green manures alone or in combination, which when incorporated decompose at different rates, release soil N at different stages to the growing crop and limit the size of the soil "N flush" after leguminous green manures are incorporated, to release soil N later in the growth of the grain crop.

Nitrogen Supply

Farmers have exploited the nitrogen-fixing role of legumes for centuries. Farmers now require more information about the management of legumes and the amounts of nitrogen they supply. Stopes *et al* (1996b) reported on a trial that investigated approaches to managing leguminous green manures in a situation that did not rely upon a livestock enterprise. The objective of the research was to provide information about which green manures accumulated most biomass (dry matter (DM)) and nitrogen under differing lengths of green manuring from 6 to 24 months. The influence on subsequent cash crop was also recorded. The results from the trial showed that one year's green manuring with pure red or white clover swards could increase both cereal yield and grain nitrogen. In this instance a pure stand of trefoil was not a successful green manure crop. The trial did not investigate the benefits of mixing the legume species.

Schmidt *et al.* (1999) confirmed that nitrogen accumulation from green manure crops was capable of supporting up to three years of cash cropping, provided that the green manure crop established well. The establishment and performance of the green manure crops has not always been reliable and therefore, for all-arable systems to be recognised, it is important that both establishment and the subsequent management of green manure crops is improved.

Green manures may be cut and mulched as many as 3 to 6 times during the season, depending upon growing conditions. Crops grown in the Elm Farm Research Centre (EFRC) all-arable research programme (Philipps *et al.*, 1999) produced an average DM production of 11.0 t/ ha, and above ground N accumulation was 240 kg/ha. The rotations that leave the green manure longer *in situ* accumulated the highest amount of DM and largest quantities of N.

The EFRC rotation trial was established in 1987 as a result of changes in the Common Agricultural Policy (CAP) and the introduction of the set-aside programme (EU Regulation No. 1765/92). Set aside, promoted with subsidies and a facility for organic farmers to use more than 5% of legumes in set aside mixtures, has increased the possibilities for fertility-building periods in all-arable systems to be longer than one year. This facility has played a major role in the conversion strategies of all-arable organic farms and many mixed organic farming systems in the UK.

Phosphorus (P) and Potassium (K)

The inter-relationships of biological activity and availability of P and K, from either soil reserves or slow release fertilisers, is not well understood. Work to understand how mycorrhizal fungi and plant associations interact with P sources is currently at very early stages, but there could be potential for improved rotational design and nutrient management strategies.

In a ley-arable rotation P and K offtakes in cash crops are balanced by the recycling of livestock manures. In predominantly arable or all-arable rotations there are not the same opportunities to replace P and K. It is therefore imperative that farmers with little or no livestock manures make best use of the manures or green waste composts by optimising the biological activity within the soil to ensure optimal P and K use from soil organic matter pools and more rapidly releasing sources. If these strategies are not maintaining the P and K supply then there are restricted fertilisers that a farmer can use upon application to their certification body. These should be seen as a last resort and not a year on year solution. It should be possible to maintain positive P and K nutrient balances by applying these strategies.

The eleven-year EFRC rotations trial (Table 4.4) showed no significant changes in the available phosphorus over time, although slow release rock phosphate had been applied to the green manure crops when soil analysis revealed a deficiency. These results are supported by the crop offtake data presented in Table 4.5.

Levels of K were not affected over the eleven years of the trial, despite the fact that no application of supplementary fertilizers or livestock residues were made. However, sandy soils with a clay content of less than 20 % may need supplementary potassium as there are insufficient clay minerals being broken down to support the K offtakes in the crops. There was no difference in soil K levels between rotations A (142.6 mg K/kg) and C (138.0 mg K/kg). However, there was a significant effect between rotation A and rotation B, in which the available K levels were 128.3 mg K/ kg.

Table 4.4. **Three experimental stockless rotations in EFRC replicated experiment 1987 to 1998**

Rotation	Course of rotation			
	1 →	2 →	3 →	4 →
A	Red Clover	Winter Wheat	Winter Wheat	Spring Oats
B	Red Clover	Potatoes	Winter Wheat	Winter Oats
C	Red Clover	Winter Wheat	Winter Beans	Winter Wheat

Nutrient budgets for other stockless or predominately arable rotations have shown some degree of variation in nutrient budgets dependent upon soil type and rotation design. Nitrogen in a well-balanced rotation should be adequately supplied; phosphorus can be maintained through soil analysis and the use of some supplementary fertilisers when appropriate; and potassium can be sustained through mineralisation of clay minerals, providing the soil type has a reasonable clay content i.e. more than 20 %, although a greater understanding of how to manage these processes requires more research.

Table 4.6 shows a nutrient budget from the ADAS Terrington stockless research programme (Stockdale *et al.*, 2001). Table 4.7 shows a nutrient budget for a commercial organic farm in the Midlands (Stockdale *et al.*, 2001).

Table 4.5. Cash crop yield and annual nutrient off-takes (N, P and K kg/ha) in the EFRC stockless rotations experiment (mean data from 1987 to 1996)

Rotation	Crop yield (t/ha)			Off-take of nutrients per course			Mean off-take per	
	Course of rotation			Course of rotation			course	rotation
	2	3	4	2	3	4		
				Nitrogen				
A	4.29[1](se±1.3)	2.64[1] (se±1.3)	2.03[1] (se±1.3)	61 (se ±2.65)	36 (se ± 3.57)	25 (se ± 0.18)	41	122
B	29.35[2](se±8.8) 14.41[3](se±3.6)	4.29[1] (se±1.3)	3.19[1] (se±1.3)	87 (se ± 0.02)	64 (se ± 3.14)	39 (se ± 0.14)	63	190
C	3.75[1](se± 1.3)	4.10[1](se± 1.1)	3.99[1](se± 1.3)	56 (se ± 3.07)	150(se ± 8.59)	57 (se ± 3.12)	88	263
				Phosphorus				
A				25 (se ± 1.93)	15 (se ± 1.53)	12 (se ± 3.60)	17	52
B				61 (se ± 4.87)	26 (se± 2.02)	19 (se ± 2.06)	35	106
C				23 (se ± 1.96)	29 (se ± 1.83)	24 (se ± 1.76)	25	76
				Potassium				
A				21 (se ± 1.04)	14 (se± 1.30)	15 (se ± 1.32)	17	50
B				153(se ± 4.18)	20(se± 1.32)	16 (se ± 1.48)	63	189
C				19 (se ± 1.06)	49 (se± 3.24)	20 (se ± 1.37)	29	88

[1]Yields adjusted to standard 15% moisture content
[2] Total yield
[3] Ware (marketable) yield

Table 4. 6. Nutrient budget (kg/ha) for ADAS Terrington stockless organic research trial (Source: Stockdale *et al.*, 2001)

Inputs	N	P	K	Outputs	N	P	K
Fixation	31.9			Crop Sales	88.8	13.1	45.2
Deposition	30.0		5	Volatilisation (from cut and mulching)	5.0		
Seed	4.3	1.2	2.6				
P Fertiliser (redzlagg)		9.3					
Total	66.2	10.5	7.6		83.8	13.1	45.2
Balance					**-17.6**	**-2.6**	**-37.6**

Table 4.7. Nutrient budget (kg/ha) for stockless rotation on a commercial farm in the UK Midlands (Source: Stockdale *et al.*, 2001).

	Winter Wheat		Spring Beans		Spring Cereal		Red Clover		Average	
	P	K	P	K	P	K	P	K	P	K
Inputs										
Deposition	0.3	2.5	0.3	2.5	0.3	2.5	0.3	2.5	0.3	2.5
Seed	0.6	1.0	1.1	2.5	0.6	0.8	0	0.1	0.6	1.1
Manure	0	0	0	0	0	0	0	0	0	0
Fertilisers	0	0	0	0	0	0	0	0	0	0
Outputs										
Crop Sales	10.6	16.8	19.0	38.0	7.7	12.0	0	0	9.3	16.7
Straw	2.1	16.8	0	0	2.0	16.0	0	0	1	8.2
Silage	0	0	0	0	0	0	0	0	0	0
Animal Products	0	0	0	0	0	0	0	0	0	0
Balance	**-11.8**	**-30.1**	**-17.7**	**-33.0**	**-8.8**	**-24.7**	**0.3**	**2.6**	**-9.5**	**-21.3**

ECONOMIC CONSIDERATIONS

Mixed organic farming systems compare well in economic terms with integrated and conventional systems (Leake, 1996). The type of livestock enterprise has a marked effect on overall profitability, with arable and dairy systems outperforming arable and beef, or arable and sheep systems (Fowler *et al.*, 2000). The profitability of all-arable organic systems, whilst outperforming non-organic systems during the cash-cropping phase of the rotation, is reduced by the income foregone in the fertility-building phase of the rotation.

Fowler *et al.* (1998 and 2000) reported that farm incomes from all-arable organic farms increased between 1995 and 1998 and were at least comparable or more profitable than non-organic all-arable systems at current crop values.

However, it is apparent that whilst IACS subsidies such as Arable Area Payments or set-aside are the same for organic or non-organic systems, profitability is highly dependent on the increased premium achieved by organic systems to support the lower yields achieved with organic grain crops such as wheat. This is less so for other organic grain crops such as beans, triticale or oats where yields are more comparable with non-organic systems (Fenwick, 2000), especially where mixtures of varieties are sown rather than monocrop stands (Welsh *et al.*, 2001).

If organic premiums are reduced, the profitability of some crops will decline due to the reduced yield potential under organic systems. Hence yield remains a key component in profitability and strategies are required to improve the yields of organic crops that have the greatest yield differential to that of the non-organic equivalent, in particular wheat.

The single biggest influencing factor on the yield potential of grain crops is soil N availability during key developmental periods. Hence the retention of soil N and manipulation of its release at appropriate stages of crop development and at different stages of the rotation is critical for success.

FUTURE DEVELOPMENTS

Red clover is the most common leguminous green manure used to build soil fertility and provide soil N for a following sequence of organic grain crops. However, more diverse use of different leguminous green manures to build fertility is required within the rotation than is currently practised. This will allow more varied weed management strategies to be used and reduce the risks of pest build-up such as stem nematode (*Ditylenchus dipsaci*) infection which can result in enforced changes to rotation design (Cormack, 1999).

A large number of leguminous green manures can be used in organic all-arable systems to fix nitrogen, many of which have differential benefits in terms of below ground biomass production, soil aeration and improving soil structure (Woodward & Burge, 1982). There is the potential to improve the protein content of organic bread making cereals by the manipulation of different green manures, timeliness of mechanical weeding operations or the use of intercropping or bi-cropping systems. More research is needed to validate these theories.

Recent changes which allow some organic farmers to utilise set-aside for livestock grazing or forage production for their own use, whilst at the same time retaining set-aside income, opens up new opportunities for income generation from the fertility-building green manure phase of the rotation, and hence a more robust and less cyclic income stream.

However, many arable-only farms no longer have the livestock management expertise, infrastructure or a willingness to re-introduce livestock enterprises, especially in the eastern regions. Co-operation between farmers to develop linked units whereby farmers with livestock expertise and winter housing infrastructure jointly develop a livestock enterprise to use the set-aside green manure ground of the other partner farm may provide one option. However, this does require a greater level of co-operation and the development of close synergistic relationships between farms than exist at present.

Current conversion strategies for arable-only farms rely heavily on income from set-aside during the fertility-building phase. Future CAP reforms may change the role or remove the provision of set-aside and hence income for this phase of the rotation as we currently know it. This will mean that different income-generating strategies must be used within the confines of organic standards. These could include the development of livestock enterprises and the introduction of livestock during a ley phase and the production of forage crops for linked farms or units.

Alternatively, where livestock enterprises are not an option there is a need to examine systems that are not reliant on cyclic ley:arable systems. This requires the further development of continuous organic crop production systems using bi-crop or intercropping strategies, whereby legumes provide the fertility for the simultaneous production of cash crops. Research is currently underway to evaluate such systems, in which grain cereals and legumes are repeatedly planted into permanent clover green manure covers using adapted direct-drilling techniques. For these systems to operate successfully, innovative cultivation and planting techniques are required, careful management of the green manure is critical and selection of appropriate crop types and varieties is essential.

As discussed above, crops with vigorous early development characteristics and tall stature (oats, triticale, winter bean, etc) are more appropriate to this type of system, whereas less competitive crops (wheat, peas, soya, etc) may provide greater challenges for integration into such systems. This is largely as a result of the growth characteristics of the commercially-available crop varieties, which have been bred for artificial fertiliser and chemical based non-organic systems.

The expansion of the small but emerging European organic plant breeding initiative, which in addition to placing primary importance on crop yield and disease resistance, will focus on characteristics such as the utilisation of slow release soil N, early crop development, crop architecture and localised suitability and adaptability, will allow the further development of such systems. If more widely adopted, these have the potential to optimise soil N use, minimise disturbance to the soil microbial biomass (by reducing the need for cultivations), and provide a mechanism for continuous organic grain crop production in all-arable based systems.

CONCLUSIONS

UK organic production systems that are predominately based on arable crop production are struggling to produce sufficient quantities of high quality food within the constraints of EC regulation 2092/91 and at the same time meet market demands. As a result the UK is becoming more reliant on imports. Barriers to conversion to organic arable production include EU production subsidies that continue to support non-organic arable system profitability, the lack of livestock management expertise, infrastructure or a willingness to re-introduce livestock enterprises, the lack of access to information on appropriate conversion strategies and the current rotational systems employed.

Research has demonstrated that all-arable and predominantly arable organic systems are agronomically and economically viable but that current conversion strategies are highly dependent on the use of annual green manures and set-aside to provide sufficient soil nitrogen and income during the fertility building phases of the rotation. The non-continuation of such payments would seriously threaten the economic viability of such organic systems in their current operational form.

Research examining alternatives to the common two-year clover-ryegrass ley conversion strategy is investigating the balance between soil nitrogen fixation, crop sale revenue and variable and fixed costs. This emphasizes the key influence of soil N on yield and the importance of organic premiums to maintain a viable income. However, any alternative conversion strategy and subsequent organic rotation is highly influenced by the farm enterprise balance, resource constraints and expertise, which can change during and after conversion and vary at a farm level or even at a field or part field level. This emphasizes the importance of designing conversion strategies and rotations that are site-specific rather than generic.

The sequence of crops in the rotation has an important influence on soil N use and for weed management as does the use of green manures to retain and release soil N over different timescales. Grain crops that develop rapidly, tiller vigorously and have a tall stature are well-suited to organic arable systems. This limits crop and variety choice with many modern varieties (particularly wheat and peas) being poorly suited to organic conditions.

Current rotation design is often sub-optimal with regard to soil N, P and K capture and utilization, with many commonly used rotations largely ignoring below ground biomass production and diversity. The use of a greater diversity of fertility building green manures within the rotation is a logical and simple next step. Recent changes to the use of set-aside also provide further utilisation options.

However, alternative strategies need to be considered which optimise soil N use, minimise disturbance to the soil microbial biomass and break the reliance on set-aside subsidies to ensure the economic viability for arable-only systems that result in a highly cyclic production system. Where livestock enterprises are not an option, choices are more limited, especially when the system requires continuous organic crop production. The use of bi-crop or intercropping strategies, in which legumes provide the fertility for the simultaneous production of cash crops may offer an appropriate alternative.

For bi-cropping and intercropping systems to operate successfully, innovative cultivation and planting techniques are required, careful management of the green manure is critical and selection of appropriate crop types and varieties is essential. Current availability of a wide range of crop varieties is a limiting factor for the success of this option, with a need for crops and varieties to be bred which are better suited to organic production conditions. The expansion of the small but emerging European organic plant breeding initiative will play an important role in developing these options further.

ACKNOWLEDGEMENTS

The authors would like to thank the Home-Grown Cereals Authority for funding this work and the technical staff at Sutton Bonington for their practical assistance. The Progressive Farming Trust is thanked for funding the EFRC Stockless Research Programme.

REFERENCES

Baars. T. (1999). Review of grassland and fodder production. *Organic Farming Research in the EU, towards the 21st Century ENOF White Book.* 77-83.

Bulson H and Stopes C.E (1995) Converting to all-arable organic farming. Presented to the 9th BOF/OGA Conference. *Food, health and the environment: the vital connections,* January 1995.

Bulson.H, Sneydon.R.W & Stopes.C (1996) The effects of plant density on intercropped wheat and field beans in an organic farming system. Elm Farm research Centre.

Bulson.H, Welsh.J, Stopes C, Woodward.L, (1996) Agronomic viability and potential economic performance of three Organic four-Year rotations without livestock, 1988-1995. In : *Aspects of Applied Biology* 47, 1996. Rotations and cropping systems.

Bulson.H, Welsh.J, Stopes C, Woodward.L, (1996) Stockless organic farming in the UK: Potential and limits 1998-1995. Proceedings of the 11th IFOAM Scientific conference: *Organic Agriculture, Down to earth and further afield.* Copenhagen, August 1996.

Cormack.W.F (1996) Terrington on the road to conversion. *New Farmer & Grower,* Winter 1996. Pp12-13.

Cormack.W.F (1997) Testing the sustainability of a stockless arable rotation on a fertile soil in Eastern England. Proceedings of the 3rd ENOF concerted action workshop, (Eds. Isart, J. and Llerena, J.J.) *'Resource Use in Organic Farming'.* Ancona, Italy, June 1997, 127-135.

Cormack.W.F (1999) Testing a stockless arable organic rotation on a fertile soil. *Designing and Testing Crop Rotations for Organic Farming, DARCOF Report No 1.* (Eds. J.E. Olesen, Eltun, R.,

Gooding, M.J., Jensen, E.S. & Kopke, U.) Borris, Denmark, June 1999, pp115-124.

David, C., Fabre, B. & Gautronneau, Y. (1996). Towards modelling the conversion of stockless farming to organic farming. On-farm research in South East of France. In *New Research in Organic Agriculture* (Eds N.H.Kristensen & H. Høgh-Jensen), pp. 23-27. IFOAM, Ökozentrum Imsbach, Tholey-Theley.

Fragstein, P. von (1996). Organic arable farming - a contradiction? In *Fourth Congress of the ESA - Book of Abstracts* (Eds. M.K. van Ittersum, G.E.G.T. Venner, S.C. van de Geijn & T.H. Jetten),Vol. 2, pp. 438-439. European Society for Agronomy; Colmar Cedex, NL.

Leake.A.R (1996) The effect of cropping sequences and rotational management: An economic comparison of conventional, integrated and organic systems. In *Rotations and Cropping Systems. Aspects of Applied Biology* 47, 1996.

Millington S, Stopes C, Woodward L and Vogtmann H (1990) Rotational Design and the limits of organic Systems – the stockless organic farm. In (Ed. Unwin R.) *Crop Protection on Organic and Low Input Agriculture. British Crop Protection Council Monograph 45*, BCPC, London.

Fenwick.R (2000) Trinidad to Siberia - NIAB Organic cereal trial results. *Organic Farming.* Winter 2000. Issue 68. pp. 16-18. The Soil Association.

Philipps.L, Welsh.J, Bulson.H, Woodward.L, (1998) Agronomic viability and potential economic performance of three Organic four-Year rotations without livestock, 1988-1998. In : Ffoguelman.D & Lockeretz W (eds) *Organic Agriculture – the credible solution for the XXIst Century'*. Proceedings of the 12th International IFOAM Scientific Conference. pp109-115.

Philipps.L, Welsh.J, Wolfe. M (1999) Ten years experience of all arable rotations. In : *Designing and Testing Crop Rotations for Organic Farming, DARCOF Report No 1.* (Eds. J.E. Olesen, Eltun, R., Gooding, M.J., Jensen, E.S. & Kopke, U.) Borris, Denmark. 14-16th June 1999, pp71-78.

National Rivers Authority. (1992). *Nitrate Reduction For Protection Zones: The Role Of Alternative Farming Systems.* Final report from Elm Farm Research Centre to NRA. R&D note 108. NRA, Bristol.

Schmidt, H., Philipps, L., Welsh, J. P. & Fragstein, P. von. (1999) Legume breaks in stockless organic farming rotations: Nitrogen accumulation and influence on the following crops. *Biological Agriculture and Horticulture*. Vol 17 pp159-170.

Stopes, C. & Millington,S. (1992) Organic Stockless Rotations. *Elm Farm Research Centre Bulletin*, No. 3, 6-8

Stopes, C. E., Millington, S. & Woodward, L. (1996a). Dry matter and nitrogen accumulation by three leguminous green manure species and the yield of a following wheat crop in organic production systems. *Agriculture, Ecosystems and Environment*. **57**, 189-196.

Stopes, C., Bulson, H., Welsh, J. & Woodward, L. (1996b*). Stockless Organic Farming - Research Review 1987-1995*. Elm Farm Research Centre; Hamstead Marshall, U.K.

Soil Association (1998) *The Organic Food and Farming Report 1998*. The Soil Association. Bristol.

Soil Association (1999) *The Organic Food and Farming Report* 1999. The Soil Association. Bristol.

Soil Association (2000) *The Organic Food and Farming Report* 2000. The Soil Association. Bristol.

Stockdale E.A. (2001) *Optimisation of phosphorus and potassium management within organic farming systems*. Final Report to MAFF OF0114.

Welsh.J.P.W (1998) *Developing strategies for weed control in organic arable systems*. PhD thesis. University of Reading.

Welsh.J.P.W (1998b) Strategies for weed control in organic arable systems. *Organic Farming*. Winter 1998. Issue 60. Pp 24-25.

Welsh.J.P.W, Bulson,H.A, Stopes.C, Froud-Williams.R.J and Murdoch.A.J (1999)The critical weed free period in organically-grown winter wheat. *Ann.Appl. Biol*. 134:315-320.

Welsh.J.P.W, Wolfe.M and Morris.M (2001) Cereal trials. A boost to variety performance knowledge. *Organic Farming*. Spring 2001. Issue 69. Pp 14-15.

Woodward.L and Burge.P (1982) *Green manures*. Elm Farm Research Centre. Practical handbook.

Younie.D and Taylor.D (1995) Maximising crop competition to minimise weeds. Paper presented at the 9th National BOF/OGA Organic conference. Cirencester January 1995. Reprinted in *New Farmer and Grower*. Winter 1995. Issue 45. pp18.

Chapter 5

Weed Control in Organic Cereals and Pulses

D. H. K. DAVIES[1] and J. P. WELSH[2]

[1]*Crop Health Department, SAC, Bush Estate, Penicuik EH26 0PH*
[2]*Elm Farm Research Centre, Hamstead Marshall, Newbury, Berkshire, RG20 0HR*

INTRODUCTION

Weeds remain one of the most significant agronomic problems associated with organic arable crop production. It is recognised that a low weed population can be beneficial to the crop as it provides food and habitat for a range of beneficial organisms (Millington *et al.*, 1990; Clements *et al.*, 1994; Aebischer, 1997; Fuller, 1997; Patriquin *et al.*, 1998). However, above critical population thresholds, weeds can significantly reduce crop yield and quality in conventional (Cussans, 1968; Hewson *et al.*, 1973; Cousens, 1985; Cudney *et al.*, 1989) and organic (Bulson, 1991) crops alike. The challenge for organic farmers is to manage weeds in such a way as to accommodate their beneficial effects whilst still producing an acceptable crop.

PREVENTATIVE WEED CONTROL TECHNIQUES

The aim of weed management strategies in organic farming is to maintain weed populations at a manageable level through a range of husbandry approaches throughout the rotation, which means that direct control actions within the individual crop have a greater surety of success. It is important to consider weeds as part of the biodiversity of the farm, so management is the general philosophy rather than eradication. Biodiversity is seen as both an indicator of ecological health, and the weeds themselves are an important food source, both directly and indirectly, for a whole range of beneficial fauna. There may be a few situations in crop seed production where the avoidance of spreading weed seeds is required; notably difficult to control or clean-out weed seeds such as wild oat, couch grass and perennial broad-leaved weeds. It is important that seed is not produced in fields with such weeds where they cannot be readily rogued out. Aside from the key strategy of not growing seed crops in seriously weedy fields, there is a wide range of weed suppressing strategies that have to be considered in an organic rotation:

- Crop rotation
- Choice of crop species
- Choice of variety/cultivars
- Use of stale and false seed beds
- Time of sowing
- Seed quality
- Seed rate
- Cultivations in darkness
- Crop architecture
- Direction of sowing
- Crop vigour
- Undersowing in cereals and mixed cropping
- Inter-cropping
- Clean harvesting
- Allelopathy

Crop rotation

Crop rotation is a key factor in determining the absolute levels of weeds in crops in the rotation, as well as having an effect on the relative abundance of different weed species. Results from rotational plot trials at SAC at two Scottish sites clearly show the impact of increasing the proportion of arable crops in the rotation on the weed seed bank (Table 5.1).

Davies *et al.* (1997), surveying the farm rotations at one of the same farms (Woodside) and another farm in Fife and comparing local conventional fields, confirmed the beneficial impact of grass in the rotation (Table 5.2).

78

Table 5.1. **Effect of percentage of arable crops in preceding years on the weed seed bank populations** (Seeds/m^2 to 20 cm depth (Source: Younie *et al.*, 1996).

% Arable Crops	Tulloch	Woodside
0	16,800	-
25	32,875	19,200
50	29,360	38,867
75	56,700	44,967

Table 5.2. **Impact of grass in the rotation on mean numbers of weed seeds per square metre to 20 cm depth over 4 seasons** (Source: Davies *et al.*, 1997).

	Year 1	Year 4
Jamesfield		
Conventional rotation *	5,710	12,167
Rotations with grass	26,092	17,782
Rotations with no grass	25,276	42,141
Woodside		
Conventional rotation*	10,500	16,000
Rotations with grass for <2years	22,140	45,857
Rotations with grass for >2years	21,688	40,438
Rotations without grass	29,500	153,999

*Conventional arable rotation, with herbicides.

Grass in the rotation for two or more years reduced weed seed banks at Jamesfield, and weed seed bank changes over early years after conversion at Woodside were greatly reduced. This was reflected in weed numbers in the crops (Table 5.3), with significant reductions in weed numbers with more than two years of grass in the rotation.

Table 5.3. **Impact of number of seasons of grass in organic rotations on weed numbers** (log $+ 1/0.25$ m^2, Source: Davies *et al.*, 1997).

Year	Number of Seasons in grass		Significance
	0	3+	
1	3.89	2.02	*
4	3.51	1.68	**
1 → 4	-0.38	-0.35	*

$* = \leq 0.05$; $** = \leq 0.01$

Further observations have shown improved weed management as both farms increased the grass component of the rotation.

Grass leys are feasible where stock plays a part in the rotation, either direct grazing or through hay or silage use. However, on many farms grass leys cannot be considered except possibly for fertility building during periods of set-aside. On such farms breaks in the arable rotation are often only one- to two-year-long green manure crops, with undersowing acting as one season.

In these cases the influence of other crops in the rotation will affect weed population increases. Bulson *et al.* (1996) showed that, after an initial red clover break, successive wheat crops gave the highest weed increase, whereas including potatoes, in which weed control can be very successful, and the more competitive oat crop in the rotation with wheat improved weed management (Table 5.4).

Winter beans in the rotation did not have a beneficial effect on weed number build-up.

Nevertheless, the long-term control of weed density within stockless rotations is difficult, and further work is required into under-cropping and break crops as aids in both annual weed management and fertility development. The control of perennial weeds appears to be a particular problem in such rotations in comparison with long grass-break rotations (Cormack, 1997). Furthermore, later crops in long runs of arable cropping will tend to be less vigorous, and therefore less competitive against weeds, allowing annual weed seed banks to build up.

Table 5.4. **Weed dry matter (DM) at harvest (g/m^2) as affected by course of rotation** (Source: Bulson *et al.*, 1996).

Course of rotation	Weed dry matter (g/m^2)
RC/WW	151
RC/WW/WW	178
RC/WW/WW/SO	115
RC/POT/WW	115
RC/POT/WW/WO	79
RC/WW/WBN/WW	129
Significance	***

Note: RC= red clover, WW= winter wheat, SO= spring oats, POT=potato, WO=winter oat, WBN=winter beans

Individual species population changes have been compared by Davies *et al.* (1997), and grass in the rotation appeared to increase meadow-grass (*Poa spp*) and possibly mayweed (*Matricaria spp*) numbers, but most annual weed species were encouraged by no grass in the rotation; notably *Polygonum spp*, fat-hen (*Chenopodium album*) and spurrey (*Spergula arvensis).

Choice of Species

The choice of crop species is usually dictated by economic factors. However, where selection can be made, the suppressive effect on weeds is an important factor. Amongst the cereals, the most competitive are probably oats and winter rye, followed by triticale, barley and wheat. Bertholdson and Jonsson (1994; *vide* Taylor *et al.*, 2001) noted that barley appears to compete with weeds mostly for below ground resources, whereas in oats and wheat competition for light seems more important (Eisele and Kopke, 1997, Lemerle *et al.*, 1996; Gooding *et al.*, 1997). However, even in barley, above ground canopy development and shading will play an important part in weed growth suppression. Nevertheless, trials at Elm Farm Research Centre (EFRC) in 2000 clearly showed the value of triticale and oats in terms of weed suppression (Figure 5.1). Winter wheat, spring wheat and spring barley were less competitive and experienced higher weed levels. In Figure 5.1, winter wheat is shaded dark; triticale and oats are light.

Figure 5.1.   **The effect of winter cereal species, variety and varietal mixture on weed cover** (%)   (Assessed July 2000).

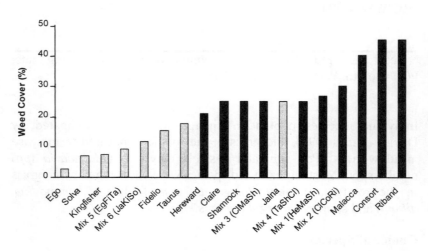

Species, Variety and Mixture

Although it is sometimes considered that spring varieties are more competitive, later sown well-established winter crops can give good suppression of spring emerging weeds. Nevertheless, the short, upright growth habit of many modern winter wheats is not suited to good weed suppression.

Amongst the pulses, field beans, once early weed competition is controlled, tend to grow over later emerging weeds and smother them out. Peas, being much shorter, are more likely to succumb to weeds. The semi-leafless nature of many modern varieties allows more light to penetrate through to the weeds.

Choice of Variety

Richards and Davies (1991), amongst others, have shown that, in conventional systems, increased early prostrate ground cover in wheat and spring barley cultivars reduced weed emergence and early growth. Eisele and Köpke (1997) confirmed that in organic systems, wheat with planophile rather than erectrophile leaves gave increased ground shading during growth, which could significantly decrease weed biomass.

It has been shown that older, taller cultivars of wheat such as Maris Widgeon also reduced the penetration of photosynthetically-active radiation into the crop (Cosser *et al.*, 1997). Reducing the plant height of Maris Widgeon through introduction of dwarfing genes, increased weediness (Cosser *et al.*, 1995). However, further trials (Cosser *et al.*, 1997) also showed that tall Maris Widgeon was not always the best variety at suppressing weeds compared with some shorter modern varieties. Eisele and Köpke (1997) also indicate that tallness is not the only or prime character, and that good overall shading ability is more important.

The new European Union funded WECOF project will attempt to evaluate the relative importance of early and later leaf angle development and height and speed of development on light penetration and weed suppression in wheat, so that farmers will be able to make better choices amongst available varieties, and breeders will more readily be able to select characteristics that favour weed suppression. It must be accepted, however, that such characteristics may prove secondary to yield benefits and disease protection, so an economic analysis of such benefits will also be undertaken within WECOF (Davies and Hoad, personal communication).

Figure 5.2.   **Wheat variety and weed biomass dry weights throughout the Growth Stages (EC) at WECOF Core Trial, Colstoun Mains 2001.**

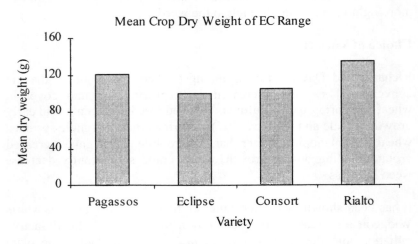

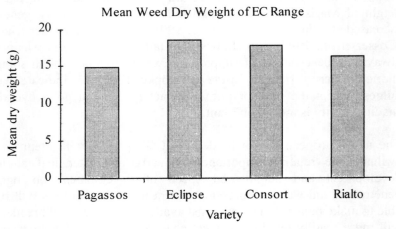

In the WECOF core trial first season, at the main UK site in East Lothian, the varieties which showed greatest weed suppression were a German variety used on organic farms, Pegassos, and the UK variety, Rialto. These varieties had the best ground cover and biomass throughout the growth of the crops. Pegassos is marginally taller than Rialto. Yield assessments had just been taken at the time of writing, and these varieties also gave the best yield (Figure 5.2). Further trials are in progress with a wider range of varieties.

There has been less work on other cereal crops, but it must be assumed that the principles that apply to wheat are likely to apply throughout cereal types. Notably that ground cover and shading are key features. Identifying and comparing suitable cultivar types amongst other cereal species will be examined within projects at SAC associated with WECOF. It is clearly evident from various workers that cultivar architecture is closely related to aspects of crop architecture in terms of weed suppression and the WECOF project also seeks to integrate these two areas.

Figure 5.3. **The effect of spring cereal species, variety and varietal mixture on weed cover** (%) (Assessed June 2000).

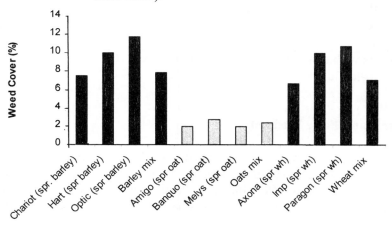

Species, Variety and Mixture

The possibility of using mixtures of varieties for weed suppression is less well researched, but work at EFRC is showing that mixtures can work as well as the best component (Figure 5.3).

There has been less work on varietal differences amongst pulses, but Grevsen (2000) in Denmark has found significant differences between pea cultivars in weed suppression (Table 5.5). The most competitive types were larger peas, and not semi-leafless.

Table 5.5. **Dry weight of weeds and number of weed plants at harvest in pea cultivars** (from Grevsen, 2000)

Cultivar	Dry weight of weeds (g/m^2)	Weeds/m^2
Dinos	160[a]	348[a]
Argona	154[a]	274[ab]
Kermit[1]	140[a]	228[ab]
Bella[1]	136[a]	261[ab]
Rani	117[ab]	273[ab]
Ambassador	88[b]	180[b]
Greenshaft	80[b]	237[ab]
Jaguar	80[b]	186[b]

Means with different superscripts are different ($P < 0.05$).
[1] semi-leafless types.

Stale and False Seedbeds

This technique involves preparing the seedbed several weeks before sowing in order to stimulate a flush of weeds, so reducing the weed seed bank likely to affect the crop. Moist conditions are essential to encourage weed emergence. The small weeds can then be removed with a very shallow harrow, flame-weeder or infra-red burner.

It is preferable if this is linked with later sowing in the spring as use too early may coincide with low soil temperatures and miss important weed emergence periods. In winter crops delayed sowing is preferred because major weed problems can be greatly reduced, and this also gives an opportunity for stale seedbed approaches. The small loss in yield possible from delayed sowing is balanced by the reduced losses due to weeds.

Time of Sowing

Early sowing of winter cereals and pulses increases weed populations significantly (Lesser *et al.*, 1996), and it is generally advised that in the UK drilling after mid-October is optimum for wheat to minimise weed competitiveness. There will be local differences, and early October may be preferred for beans for weather reasons where soil types are heavy, and generally in northern and western regions.

In spring cereals and pulses, allowing time for a stale seedbed approach (see above) assists in reducing weed problems in the crop. Otherwise it is difficult to avoid weed emergence with the crop.

Seed Quality

It is clear that good crop establishment and early vigour, important for weed suppression, is linked to the quality of seed used. Currently, undressed conventional seed can be used with derogation (up to 31 December 2003) because of the limited organic seed availability, although that is changing. If farmers use their own seed, there may be a problem. A small trial at Elm Farm Research Centre (EFRC) has shown lower germination and vigour in home-saved spring wheat than in untreated brought-in conventional seed.

The fact that seed remains untreated has presented problems where head diseases are widespread. In the 2000 growing season, German and French seed producers found high levels of *Fusarium* in wheat seed, which entailed more conventional seed being used than expected. Seed testing for diseases is critical so that best selections between stocks can be made, even at the farm level. Meanwhile, EFRC has set up the "Seeds for the Future" initiative to improve breeding and production to overcome these problems.

Cultivations in the Dark

Hartmann and Nezadal (1990; *vide* Ascard, 1993) found that weed populations were considerably reduced when all soil cultivations were done at night. The theory behind this is that many weeds need light signals to germinate. This has been re-examined by a number of workers, such as Ascard (1993) in Sweden. EFRC in England have looked at putting a light-proof cover over a power harrow/drill combination (Welsh *et al.*, 1999). The results are variable, with on occasion up to 70% reduced germination, but sometimes, in dry soils, little difference with cultivation in the light. Furthermore, there can be increases in species not affected by the light.

The value of the reductions in weed population has been shown by Welsh *et al.* (1999) to be transitory, with little final biomass or yield benefit from the treatment. A more consistent result from the practice has to be proven before it can be considered for widespread use.

Seed Rates and Sowing Pattern

It has been recognised for a long time through observation that crops grown at higher seed rates tend to compete more effectively with weeds. However, there is not always a matching yield benefit, and the extra seed cost then has to be matched with the extra weed control benefit.

For example, Younie and Taylor (1995) found that increasing seed rate in spring oats from 150 to 300 kg/ha had a significant impact on weed growth, greater than that of narrow row spacings (Figure 5.4; Table 5.6). The effect was apparent as early as late May, with 94% and 22% more weed biomass in the 150kg/ha and 225kg/ha seed rate respectively than in 300kg/ha. There was no yield difference between 225 and 300kg/ha seed rate, but it was reduced at the lower rate. Increased weed suppression at higher seed rates was reflected in increased leaf area index and light infiltration of the canopy (Table 5.7).

Figure 5.4. **The effect of oat seed rate (mean of 2 sites, 1994) on weed development** (Younie & Taylor, 1995)

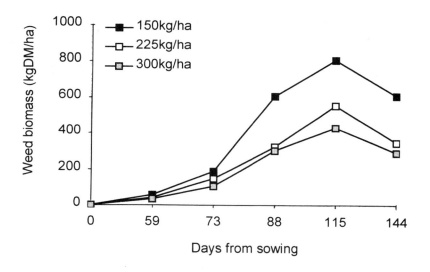

Table 5.6. **Effect of seed rate and row spacings (mean of 2 sites) on spring oat grain yield** (Source: Younie and Taylor, 1998)

	Grain yield (tonnes/ha @ 85% dry matter)
Seed rate (kg/ha)	
150	5.32
225	5.65
300	5.66
Row spacing (cm)	
9	5.54
13.5	5.68
18	5.43

Table 5. 7.   Effect of seed rate on crop leaf area index and percentage of incident light infiltrating oat canopy in early June (Mean of two sites).

Seed rate (kg/ha)	Leaf Area Index	Percentage light infiltration to 10cm above ground
150	4.68	58.3
225	5.66	56.1
300	6.54	49.9

In wheat, Dover and East (1990) found that increasing seed rates from 300 up to 450 seeds/m^2 (250 kg/ha) reduced pre-harvest weed populations slightly, without any yield variation.

Griepentrog *et al.* (2000) also found that increasing wheat seed rates from 200 to 660 seeds/m^2 greatly increased weed suppression. However, sowing in a cross pattern at 12 to 8 cm, compared with a normal row pattern at the same width, suppressed weed biomass by a further 30%. Yield also increased by 60% over normal row pattern at 400 seeds/m^2.

Work under the European Union WECOF project, started in 2000, includes row width in organic wheat as a key factor in weed suppression. Provisional Scottish results indicate that a row width of about 16 cm gives better weed suppression than narrower or wider row widths, but these trials are being repeated over two further seasons. (Davies and Hoad, personal communication).

Amongst the pulses, Grevsen (2000) in Denmark found that increasing seed rate of pea cultivars from 90 to 150 seeds/m^2 reduced the dry weight of weed plants by 40%. Seed weight and leaf type were important, as was early growth vigour of cultivars (Table 5.5). Vine length was not, however, correlated with weed weight, conflicting with results from Canada by Wall and Townsley-Smith (1996; *vide* Creusen, 2000). Early growth is likely to be critical in other pulses, but possibly, in beans, canopy development over a longer period may be of importance.

Direction of Sowing

Eisele and Kopke (1997) noted that increased shading ability in taller wheat varieties could only be seen when sown in an E-W direction, compared with a N-S direction. The importance of direction, hypothesised by a number of workers, may be dependent on variety. Its importance may also be dependent on latitude. As a consequence the EU WECOF project has integrated direction of sowing into the core work on variety type and row width, with sites from Spain to Scotland to resolve the issues involved.

Table 5.8. **Impact of direction of sowing on percent weed ground cover under wheat varieties at GS49** (Source: Davies & Hoad, unpublished).

| | Row Width | | | |
	Narrow	**Medium**	**Wide**	**Mean**
E-W Sowing				
Pegassos	8.4	20.6	16.3	15.1
Eclipse	18.1	19.1	26.9	21.4
Consort	20.3	17.8	41.6	26.6
Rialto	13.4	14.7	23.1	17.1
			Overall	20.1
N-S Sowing				
Pegassos	13.0	12.8	6.9	10.9
Eclipse	28.4	24.5	24.5	25.8
Consort	14.6	12.3	19.1	15.3
Rialto	18.0	12.4	16.3	15.6
			Overall	22.5

Initial results from a Scottish site do not show a clear response to direction of sowing in terms of crop growth and weed suppression. There is a complex interaction with row width and variety, and only a tendency for E-W sowing to show benefits at narrow row widths at

Growth Stage 49 in ¾ varieties, but at wide row widths, N-S sowing may have given better response (Table 5.8). However, this varies with variety and growth stage, and further trials are planned to confirm these trends.

We have no evidence for peas and beans, but beans sown in drills may also show a benefit to E-W drilling in terms of weed control in the row.

Crop Vigour

Crop vigour has been noted by several workers to be of importance in early competition with weeds. This is in part a varietal factor, as noted by Creusen (2000) for peas, and in terms of early prostrate ground cover as noted for cereals by Richards and Davies (1991). In part, it is also related to the quality of the seed, as has been noted earlier in this paper.

However, continuing crop vigour is related to soil, weather factors, and nutritional status. Weather factors are not controllable, but good seedbed conditions will assist in good crop establishment and long-term root growth. Nutritional status of the soil affects both the growth of the crop and the weeds. It is evident that crops further from the nutrition-building phase of the rotation will have less available nitrogen, and such crops will be less vigorous (Table 5.9) and potentially less competitive against weeds.

Table 5.9.   Effect of years after clover break on yield of wheat (from Cormack, 1997)

Rotation	Yield of wheat (tonnes/ha @ 85% DM)
Clover/Clover/Potatoes/Wheat (1)	6.3
Clover/Clover/Wheat	9.8
Clover/Clover/Potatoes/Wheat (2)	6.7

Although not from organic systems research, Grundy *et al.* (1993) clearly showed the impact of nitrogen availability on weed growth in wheat crops (Table 5.10), as a result of increased crop vigour and growth. Grundy *et al.* (1993) also found that the reduction in weeds was greater where high N availability was linked with high sowing densities.

Table 5.10. **Weed density in response to additions of nitrogen in wheat** (from Grundy *et al.*, 1993)

Kg N/ha	Weed density/m^2
0	143.2
40	124.4
160	36.0
SE	15.3
P	P<0.001

It is clear that certain weed species are highly nitrophilic, and others much less so. This will probably have an impact on the mix of weed species present in fully converted systems. By observation, nitrophilic species such as cleavers and brome species are much less of a problem in organic than conventional systems. But those apparently less dependent on high nitrogen levels over winter and early spring such as dead nettle, knot-grass, fat-hen and mayweed, are at least as great a problem, and with less vigorous crops, probably more of a problem than in conventional systems. In Denmark, Jørnsgård *et al.* (1996) have confirmed these observations by showing that some weeds, including fat-hen and dead nettle, have lower nitrogen 'optima' than the crop, indicating that they would be relatively more competitive at lower nitrogen status. The importance of timely weed control is organic crops is clear, with some evidence that control measures as nitrogen becomes available in the spring are crucial.

Undersowing and Mixed Cropping

Intersowing wheat crops with subterrananean clover in Italy and undersowing with clover in France has been shown to reduce weed biomass (Barberi *et al.*, 1998, *vide* Taylor *et al.*, 2000; Lambin *et al.*, 1994, *vide* Taylor *et al.*, 2000). In practice in the UK it is usually spring barley or oats that are undersown with clover or grass/clover, and these are less weedy before and after harvest than when there is no undersowing (Younie, 2001).

Mixed cropping with pulses may also reduce weed growth, but Eisele (1998; *vide* Taylor *et al.*, 2000)) showed that *Vicia hirsuta* (hairy tare) can severely reduce crop yields, so care must be taken to miminise competition with the cereal. Recent work at SAC with vetch and spring barley shows similar results (Younie, personal communication). However, where mixed crops are grown to provide high protein feeds, such mixtures appear to be good at reducing weed growth. Clements *et al.* (1997) have developed a conventional whole-crop silage system with clover and wheat, and found that herbicides were not needed for broad-leaved weed control.

Table 5.11. **Weed biomass (g m^{-2}) as affected by bean and wheat density** (from Bulson *et al.*, 1991).

		Wheat %				
		0	**25**	**50**	**75**	**100**
Beans %	**0**	434	302	146	97	124
	25	398	168	148	96	124
	50	346	162	133	80	100
	75	284	138	151	75	36
	100	169	117	72	83	62

Bulson *et al.* (1991) inter-cropped organic autumn sown field beans and wheat, found yield benefits, and significant reductions in weed biomass, with the optimum being around 75% recommended density of beans and 75 to 100% of wheat (Table 5.11).

Pea, vetch, bean barley and oat mixtures have long been a common feature of arable/livestock rotations. These are generally less weedy than individual component crops. Sowing crops into prepared stands of a legume (i.e. bi-cropping) has been examined by a number of workers e.g. Clements *et al.* (1997), with the legume as the nitrogen-donating part of the rotation. In these situations annual weeds do not present a problem, although long established ground cover can develop perennial weed problems.

Allelopathy

Many plant species produce chemicals that affect the development of plants growing in their immediate environment. This is called allelopathy. A wide range of species has been found to produce allelopathy, but it is not widely used in agriculture. The use of rye, cut and left, prior to sowing soyabean has been used in the USA. Morris and Parish (1991) found that sunflower residue can inhibit weed growth, but also wheat growth in minimum-till situations. This is being examined further in the current EU- WECOF project. However, in much of the UK sunflowers have no potential as a break crop before wheat, and other crops require further investigation.

Cleanliness

A number of hygiene practices are recommended to reduce weed problems. In general equipment should be washed down after operation in very weedy fields. Weeds should not be allowed to flower and blow seed onto cropping areas.

REACTIVE WEED CONTROL

Reactive weed control mainly relates to some form of mechanical intervention in the growing crop. Mechanical weed control in organic cereal and pulse crops can be split broadly into two methods- selective (e.g. inter-row hoeing or brush weeders) and non-selective (e.g. spring-tine weeding or harrowing). A survey of EFRC's arable farmer group members found that spring-tine weeders, such as the

Harrowcomb or Einbock, were the most widely practiced form of mechanical weed control in organic cereal crops in the UK, whilst inter-row hoeing was very uncommon (EFRC, 1997). The survey also highlighted that mechanical weed control tended to be conducted in the spring rather than in the autumn period.

When deciding on a reactive weed control strategy, it is important to consider a number of key factors:

1.   *Weed threshold.* Is the weed infestation of sufficient size to affect significantly the current crop in terms of grain yield and quality and consequently crop gross margin and net farm income? If I decide not to control the weeds, will the seed that they produce significantly affect future crops?
2.   *Timing.* If the weed population is of sufficient size to warrant control, what is the best time to implement control to achieve the maximum benefit to the crop?
3.   *Method.* Which method of weed control is likely to be the most effective at removing weeds at the appropriate time?

Weed thresholds

Orson (1990) emphasised the difficulties in developing a weed threshold system due to the highly complex nature of quantifying crop-weed interactions. Each species will vary in its competitiveness, which in turn will be influenced by the competitiveness of the crop, date of emergence in relation to the crop, weather conditions, soil type and nutrient status. It is recognised that the competitiveness of weeds and the dormancy of their seeds depend to a large extent on soil type and the weather conditions that follow the time when weeds have to be removed in order to prevent or minimise yield loss.

There has been a considerable research effort over the last few years to identify weed threshold levels in non-organic crops. However, very few studies have aimed to do the same for organic crops. It is clear that conditions in organic crops are different from those encountered in non-organic crops and, for the reasons give above, it is likely that weed threshold levels will also be different. This remains an area where further research is needed, although Bond and Lennartsson (1999) commented that for most organic crops, weed control would be justified.

Timing

To identify the most appropriate time to control weeds it is important to know when weeds are likely to exert their greatest competitive effect on the crop and/or when the crop can least tolerate the presence of weeds. As a rule of thumb, in autumn/winter-sown crops, it is the autumn germinating weeds that pose the most serious problems and, likewise, in spring-sown crops, weeds that germinate at a similar time to the crop are likely to be the most problematic. Therefore, in general, ensuring the crop is kept as weed free as possible during its early growth stages is likely to be the most beneficial strategy. Once crops become established, they should then be able to compete effectively with emerging weeds. Clearly, as has been shown already, some crop species are better competitors than others. This rule of thumb has been reinforced by another approach that can address this question, the identification of the critical weed-free period, first suggested by Nieto *et al.* (1968).

The critical weed-free period represents the time interval between two separately measured components: the maximum weed-infested period or the length of time that weeds which have emerged with the crop can remain before they begin to interfere with crop growth; and the minimum weed free period or the length of time a crop must be free of weeds after planting in order to prevent yield loss (Weaver *et al.*, 1992). These components are experimentally determined by measuring crop yield loss as a function of successive times of weed removal or weed emergence respectively.

Very few studies have considered this in organic farming systems. Welsh *et al.* (1999) reported some initial results for the critical weed-free period in organically grown winter wheat (Figure 5.5). The results suggested that with a mixed weed infestation of blackgrass and mayweed the critical weed-free period would begin at 645 °C days (°Cd) after sowing (December) and end at 1223 °C days after sowing (March). Therefore, in the case of winter wheat, keeping the crop free of weeds from shortly after sowing to the early spring is the most effective strategy. This is in contrast to current practice, where most weeding operations start in the spring period, by which time the crop will have already suffered a significant yield penalty (20 to 25% reduction). It should be noted, however, that this was the result from only one season at one site.

Figure 5.5. **Observed and fitted wheat grain yield in 1995/96 (% of predicted weed-free control) as affected by the duration of the weed-infested period (O) (SE = ±17.3) and weed-free period (●) (SE = ±17.4).**

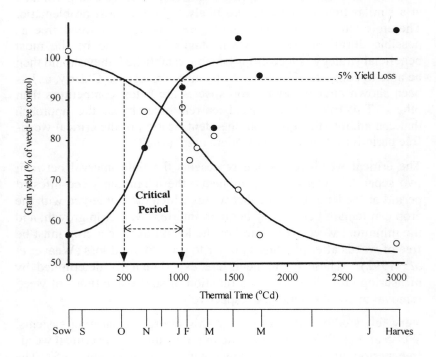

Unfortunately, there has not been a similar study for field beans or peas, but it is anticipated that weed control should be focused at the start of the growing season whilst the crop becomes established.

Method of weed control

Experiments conducted by Jones *et al.* (1996) investigated the most effective ways of killing annual weeds mechanically. The experiments comprised a range of cutting and burial treatments. Their findings indicated that the most effective means of control was achieved either by cutting weed stems at the soil surface or by totally burying them with soil. The moisture content of the soil was also shown to be an important factor in determining the effectiveness of treatment such that control was better under dry soil conditions. This is supported by Terpstra and Kouwenhoven (1981), who reported that under dry soil conditions hoeing resulted in 96% weed control, whilst under moist conditions the level of control decreased to 84%.

Spring-tine weeders

Spring-tine weeders (e.g Einbock or Harrowcomb) rely on the many tines to create a tilth to bury weeds and rip them out of the soil resulting in desiccation (Kouwenhoven and Terpstra, 1979; Terpstra and Kouwenhoven, 1981; Rasmussen and Svenningsen, 1995).

Spring-tine weeders are available in a range of working widths (typically from 6m to 24m), although they are all basically the same design. They comprise modular frames, which are suspended from the main frame by means of chains. Suspending the modular frames in this way allows each of them to follow the contours of the ground independently of the main frame. Each of the modular frames is equipped with rows of "L"-shaped spring-tines. The tines are available in a range of diameters, depending on the intensity of treatment required, with the larger diameter tines resulting in a greater intensity of treatment.

The angle of the tines can also be adjusted to increase or decrease the intensity of weeding treatment. Angling the tines forward increases the pressure on the tine, consequently increasing the intensity of treatment, whilst angling the tines backward has the opposite effect.

Inter-row hoes

As the name implies, cultivation only occurs between the crop rows, in contrast to spring-tine weeding where the entire area is cultivated.

Weed control results from undercutting the weed plants and either leaving them on the soil surface to desiccate or burying them in soil (Terpstra and Kouwenhoven, 1981).

There are numerous types of inter-row hoe available, although their mode of action is principally the same. Generally, the inter-row hoe comprises a tool bar to which the inter-row hoeing units are attached. The units have independent suspension to allow the hoe blades to follow the surface contour, resulting in a consistent depth of cultivation. The hoe blades are mounted to the units via either a rigid or sprung leg. There is also a variety of cultivating tools for inter-row weeding, from standard A-blades to rolling cultivators.

Both the depth and angle of the hoe blade can be adjusted. Both increasing the blade angle (from the horizontal) and increasing its depth of cultivation result in more soil movement and consequently more aggressive weed control. The angle of rotary cultivators can also be adjusted to give more or less soil movement.

Key factors influencing mechanical weed control

Böhrnsen (1993) cited eight key factors that influenced the efficacy of mechanical weeding techniques:

1. Soil type
2. Soil moisture
3. Soil surface structure
4. Working principles of the weed control machinery
5. Driving speed
6. Weed species specific robustness
7. Growth stage of weeds and cultivated plants
8. Weather after the mechanical weed control treatment

Soil type and condition

Soil type and condition are expected to affect any weed control technique that relies on tillage. There is, however, currently little data in the literature that relates the efficacy of mechanical weed control to these factors although it is possible to speculate on the likely effects that soil type/condition will have. Spring-tine weeding will tend to be more severely constrained by soil type/condition than inter-row hoeing (Rasmussen, 1993c; Stöppler-Zimmer, 1994). For example, the relatively light tines of the spring-tine weeder are less likely to penetrate the soil if it is crusted or hard than the more robust and heavier hoe blades.

Driving speed and direction

A study by Rydberg (1994) investigated the influence of driving direction and driving speed of harrowing on weeds and cultivated plants. The study was conducted in an oat crop and treatments were implemented at the 3 to 4 leaf stage. The level of weed control was found to be dependent on driving speed although most of the reduction in weed levels was achieved at 5 km/h. Harrowing across the crop rows did not provide significantly better levels of weed control than harrowing along the rows. Neither speed nor direction of harrowing significantly affected oat grain yield.

The major limitation of inter-row hoeing is its speed of operation. Because the hoe has to be guided accurately between the crop rows, forward speed is limited to ensure accuracy. There is, however, some very recent work that has looked at developing automated guidance systems for inter-row hoeing (Tillett and Hague, 1999). The first commercial version of this machine has recently been released and it promises to allow significantly greater speeds of operation, greater accuracy and increased workable hours as the tractor driver will be less fatigued from having to concentrate on accurate driving.

Weed species and growth stage

Weed species and growth stage are also important factors in determining the efficacy of mechanical weed control. Berry (1994) found that different weeders removed some species more readily than others. Similarly, a review by Stöppler-Zimmer (1994) found that individual weed species demonstrated differing responses to mechanical weed control. Cleavers (*Galium aparine*) and common hemp-nettle (*Galeopsis tetrahit*) were controlled more effectively than either mayweed (*Matricaria recutita*) or red dead-nettle (*Lamium purpureum*) by harrowing. Also, harrowing generally offers poor control of grass weeds (Blair *et al*., 1997). In contrast, the efficacy of inter-row hoeing is less sensitive to weed species than harrowing due to its more robust nature.

Böhrnsen (1993) reported that small weeds (< 3-leaf stage; 60 to 85% reduction) were controlled much more effectively by harrowing than large weeds (> 3-leaf stage; 33 to 63% reduction), whilst inter-row hoeing controlled weeds effectively (90% density reduction) at a wide range of growth stages. Both Wilson *et al.* (1993) and Welsh *et al.* (1997) found that tap rooted weeds, e.g. field poppy (*Papaver rhoeas*) and shepherds purse (*Capsella bursa-pastoris*), were controlled most effectively at an early weed growth stage before their tap-roots established. Shallow-rooted weeds, however, e.g chickweed (*Stellaria media*) or cleavers, with a more scrambling or climbing habit were controlled best at later growth stages when they could be "raked" out of the crop.

Weather after treatment

Weather after the weeding operation is also likely to have a large effect on its efficacy. Wet weather after treatment, especially with those weeders relying on desiccation as a means of weed kill, will decrease the effectiveness of control, as weeds may re-root (Terpstra and Kouwenhoven, 1981).

Selectivity

Rasmussen (1990) introduced the concept of selectivity as a means of evaluating a range of harrows, where selectivity was defined as the ratio between weed control and crop burial in soil. Selectivity is the key factor that determines the possibilities for achieving high degrees of weed control without serious crop damage. Theoretically, spring-tine weeding can control weeds completely if it is done with adequate intensity during early crop growth stages, but this is rarely possible without causing significant reductions in crop yield (Rasmussen, 1991, 1992).

Rasmussen (1991) found that the selectivity of harrowing was influenced by the composition of the weed flora, site characteristics and degree of weed control, whilst there were no differences in selectivity between the harrows used. Rasmussen (1993b) also highlighted that inter-row hoeing was a highly selective method of weed control in comparison to harrowing.

Efficacy of mechanical weed control

Spring-tine weeding

Spring-tine weeding can be carried out at three stages during the growing season: pre-crop emergence, early post-crop emergence and late post-crop emergence. Although Rasmussen (1996) suggested that pre-emergence soil cultivation after crop planting has the potential to control early germinating weeds, it may create weed problems by stimulating subsequent weed seed germination (Roberts and Potter, 1980; Mohler and Galford, 1997).

Early post-crop emergence weed control is performed a few weeks after emergence. For cereals, the recommendation is to harrow once the crop gets to the 3-leaf stage. At this time, the main problem is the low selectivity of control between crop and weeds. Weeds at this stage are mainly controlled by burial with soil, however, the crop is also vulnerable to soil coverage at this time (Rasmussen, 1996). Thus Wilson *et al.* (1993), found that autumn weeding treatments with a tine harrow reduced crop cover from 80% to 70%.

Rasmussen (1995) reported that spring-tine weeders could be used at later crop growth stages than other types of harrow. When weeding is conducted parallel to the crop rows in the late stages of cereal development, the tines tend to be forced into the inter-row spaces due to the resistance offered by the crop rows. If the tines are long enough, inter-row spring-tine weeding can be carried out from late tillering until crop maturity. The use of spring-tine weeders in this way has been defined as selective harrowing, which works by uprooting weeds, tearing them apart and burying them in soil, without the associated crop damage.

Reductions in weed density as a result of spring-tine weeding range from 5% to 90% depending on the weed species present (Rasmussen,

1991, 1992, 1993b; Wilson *et al.*, 1993; Peruzzi *et al.*, 1993; Rasmussen and Svenningsen, 1995).

It is clear, therefore, that harrowing with a spring-tine weeder has the potential to reduce weed levels but its impact on crop yield is more ambivalent. For example, Popay *et al.* (1992) working in wheat and barley in New Zealand reported that spring-tine weeding reduced weed density and weed dry matter but had no effect on crop yield. Similarly, Samuel and Guest (1990) found that harrowing in the spring reduced the population of speedwell (*Veronica hederifolia*) by as much as 90% but there was no benefit in terms of crop yield. Peruzzi *et al.* (1993) also reported a 40% reduction in weed density as a result of spring-tine weeding but again crop yield was not significantly affected.

Although spring-tine weeding can reduce weed density, it rarely produces significant and positive crop yield responses. Rasmussen (1993b) suggested that this might be due to a number of factors:

1. Initial weed infestation below a competitive level.
2. Insufficient level of weed control.
3. Damage to the crop by the mechanical weeding operations.

Other factors, however, such as the timing of weed removal in relation to the critical weed free period and subsequent weed emergence following mechanical control are also likely to affect crop yield response to weeding.

Inter-row hoeing

In contrast to spring-tine weeding, inter-row hoeing is a selective method of mechanical weed control (Rasmussen, 1993a, 1993c). Also, inter-row hoeing is particularly effective at controlling mature weeds (Böhrnsen, 1993; Morrish, 1995), whereas spring-tine weeding is most effective when weeds are small and consequently more vulnerable to soil cover (Wilson *et al.*, 1993; Böhrnsen, 1993).

Work by Hammarström *et al.* (1993) demonstrated that hoeing winter wheat with ducks-foot blades at 25 cm row spacing could reduce the density of weeds between the rows by 82% and weed biomass by 35%. The weed density in the crop row was reduced by 25%. He also found that it was possible to hoe at a normal crop row spacing of 12.5 cm using a rotary hoe. At this row spacing, weed density was reduced by approximately 45% between the rows and 25% in the rows. Crop yields were slightly increased as a result of hoeing with both the ducks-foot blades and the rotary hoe when compared with the unweeded control sown on 12.5 cm rows, although the increases were not statistically significant.

Similarly, Böhrnsen *et al.* (1993) reported that inter-row hoeing could reduce weed density by 90%, whilst spring-tine weeding only resulted in a 35% reduction in weed density. Crop yield, however, was only slightly improved by inter-row hoeing in comparison with the unweeded control.

A limitation of inter-row hoeing is that the crop has to be planted on a wider row spacing, which might be expected to increase the level of intra-specific competition within the crop and consequently limit grain yield. Hammarström *et al.* (1993), however, found no significant difference in grain yield between the unweeded controls at a crop row spacing of 12.5 cm and 25 cm. Also, Rasmussen (1993a) reported that crop yields at a 20 cm row spacing were significantly higher than crop yields at a 12 cm row spacing, although he thought this could be due to the higher density of plants established at 20 cm row spacing as a result of higher seed rates.

Weed dry matter was found to be higher in crop sown on 20 or 25 cm rows compared with 12 or 12.5 cm rows (Rasmussen, 1995; Hammarström *et al.*, 1993). This is probably as a consequence of the decreased competitive ability of the crop at the wide row spacing.

In contrast to spring-tine weeding, inter-row hoeing tends to result in greater reductions of weed density and its efficacy is less affected by the growth stage of the weeds. Yield responses to inter-row hoeing, however, are still variable with few reports of statistically significant positive yield responses.

Problematic Weeds

Perennial weeds (couch, creeping thistle, docks etc) are probably the most problematic for organic agriculture. In-crop mechanical weed control is generally poor at controlling this type of weed. Perennial weeds are best controlled on a rotational basis, making use of cover crops as well as the cultivations between different phases of rotation. In extreme cases it may be necessary to fallow the field to allow a series of rigid-tined cultivations.

Of the annual species, wild oats can also be difficult to control and are certainly a potentially serious problem for those engaged in organic seed production. However, there have been some very innovative solutions to minimising the problem. For example, the use of a converted rape swather, with the cutter-bar set above the height of the crop, to remove wild oat seed heads (Steele, 1997).

Secondary effects of mechanical weed control

Soil

Mattsson *et al.* (1990) reported a number of advantages of inter-row weeding, other than weed control. Inter-row weeding breaks up the soil crust allowing aeration of the soil and possibly improves the water holding capacity of some soils. Also, soil tillage, through mechanical weed control, may lead to an increased nitrogen concentration in the soil by exposing less accessible substrates to mineralisation by microbes (Dowdell *et al.*, 1983; Böhrnsen, 1993; Smith *et al.* 1994). It is likely that inter-row hoeing will be more effective than spring-tine weeding at producing this effect due to the greater soil movement that occurs with this method.

Fauna

Mechanical weeding may also have detrimental side effects such as damage to populations of beetles, other soil fauna, and ground-nesting birds (Jones *et al.*, 1996). Careful consideration must, therefore, be given to the timing and frequency of weeding operations to minimise the impact on the environment.

SUMMARY

- Crop rotation is the key to long-term management of weeds. In particular grass breaks give the best results. Clover breaks and crops in which weeds are easy to manage are important for stockless rotations.
- Amongst cereals, triticale and oats are more competitive than wheat or barley.
- Cereal and pea varieties vary in ability to shade out weeds. Which are the best shading attributes is still being resolved, but either early or late shading may be acceptable.
- Use of stale seedbeds is a very useful way of reducing weed emergence in the following crop.
- Early sowing in autumn increases weed pressures. In the spring allow time for stale seedbed approaches.
- Good seed quality gives good crops. The new EFRC Seeds for the Future Intiative will improve breeding and production of organic seed.
- A more consistant result from cultivations in the dark to reduce weed emergence is required before it can be widely advised.
- Increasing seed rates improves competition with weeds, but check the cost against that of extra cultivations.
- Sowing in an E-W direction may give extra weed suppression in taller varieties, but this may vary with latitude and row width, and further research is needed.
- Good crop vigour improves weed suppression. Crops further from the nutrition-building phase tend to be less competitive.
- Inter-sowing or undersowing crops gives good suppression of annual weeds. Mixed cropping of cereals and pulses are also more competitive than each crop alone.
- The use of allelopathy for weed suppression still requires further research for UK conditions. Sunflower and rye residues have shown benefits in other countries, but inhibition of the crop is also possible.
- If you have been working in a weedy field, wash off equipment before moving to other fields.

- The identification of weed thresholds should help to rationalize weed control (i.e. to weed or not to weed). At present, however, there is little information available.
- Weed control in the growing crop should be timed to remove weeds during the early part of the growing season, to allow the crop to become established and competitive against emerging weeds.
- Spring-tine weeding is most effective on friable soils where it can produce sufficient tilth to bury weeds. In general, weeds should be controlled at an early growth stage before they become established. Control of mature broad-leaved weeds, perennial weeds and grasses is poor.
- Inter-row hoeing, due to its more robust mode of action, is less sensitive to soil type and conditions and can work well on heavier soils or on soils that tend to cap. Also, it can control annual broad-leaved and grass weeds at a wide range of weed growth stages. The control of perennial weeds is still difficult and these weeds should be dealt with during the primary and secondary cultivations before drilling. The major limitation of inter-row hoeing is its work rate, although this has recently been addressed by automated guidance hoeing systems.
- Mechanical weed control may also have the added benefit of stimulating the mineralisation of soil-bound nitrogen, which, if timed with the crops peak demand for nitrogen, could help to improve crop yield and quality.

REFERENCES

Aebischer N J. (1997). Effects of cropping practices on declining farmland birds during the breeding season. *Proceedings of the 1997 Brighton Crop Protection Conference – Weeds.* 915-922.

Ascard, J. (1993). Soil cultivation in darkness reduced the emergence of weeds. Abstract *ISHS International Symposium*, 1993, Ulvik, Norway

Berry M P. (1994). Mechanical and non-chemical weed control in organic and low input cereal production. *PhD thesis, Wye College, University of London.*

Blair A M, Jones P A, Orson J H & Casely J C. (1997). Integration of row widths, chemical and mechanical weed control and the effect on winter wheat yield. *Aspects of Applied Biology 50 – Optimising Cereal Inputs: Its Scientific Basis.* 385-392.

Böhrnsen A. (1993). Several years results about mechanical weed control in cereals. *Communications of the fourth International Conference IFOAM – Non-Chemical Weed Control,* Dijon. 93-100.

Böhrnsen A, Becker K & Wagner M. (1993). Mechanische pflege mit striegel und hacke. *Landtechnik* **48**: 174-177.

Bond W & Lennartsson M E K. (1999). Organic weed control – back to the future. *Proceedings of the 1999 Brighton Crop Protection Conference – Weeds.* 929-938.

Bulson H A J. (1991). Intercropping wheat with field beans in organic farming systems. *Ph.D. Thesis, University of Reading.*

Bulson H A J, Welsh J P, Stopes C E & Woodward L. (1996). Agronomic viability and potential economic performance of three organic four year rotations without livestock, 1988-1995. *Aspects of Applied Biology 47, Rotations & Cropping Systems.* 277-286.

Clements D R, Stephan F W & Swanton C J. (1994). Integrated weed management and weed species diversity. *Phytoprotection* **75**: 1-18.

Clements R O, Donaldson G, Purvis G & Burke J. (1997). Clover: cereal bi-cropping. *Aspects of Applied Biology* **50,** *Optimising cereal inputs: Its scientific basis.* 249-254.

Cormack, W F. (1997). Testing the sustainability of a stockless arable rotation on a fertile soil in Eastern England. *Proceedings Third ENOF Workshop,* Ancona, 127-135.

Cosser N D, Gooding M T, Davies, W P, Thompson A J & Froud-Williams R J (1997). Cultivar and Rht gene influences on the competitive ability, yield, breadmaking qualities of organically grown winter wheat. *Aspects of Applied Biology* **50,** *Optimising cereal inputs: Its scientific basis.* 39-52.

Cosser N D, Gooding J M & Froud-Williams R J (1996). The impact of wheat cultivar, sowing date and grazing on the weed seedbank of an organic farming system. . *Aspects of Applied Biology* **47**, *Rotations & Cropping Systems.* 429-432.

Cousens R. (1985). An empirical model relating crop yield to weed and crop density and a statistical comparison with other models. *Journal of Agricultural Science* **105**: 513-521.

Cudney D W, Lowell S J, Holt J S & Reints J S. (1989). Competitive interactions of wheat (*Triticum aestivum*) and wild oats (*Avena fatua*) grown at different densities. *Weed Science* **37**: 538-543.

Cussans F E. (1968). The growth and development of *Agropyron repens* (L.) Beauv. In competition with cereal, field beans and oilseed rape. *Proceedings of the 9th British Weed Control Conference*, Brighton. 131-136.

Davies D H K, Christal A C, Talbot M, Lawson H M & Wright G M. (1997). Changes in weed population in the conversion of two arable farms to organic agriculture. *Proceedings 1997 Brighton Crop Protection Conference – Weeds*, 1997, 973-978.

Dover P A & East J. (1990). The effects of variety blends and seedrates on disease and weed incidence in wheat grown in organic systems. *BCPC Monograph 45: Crop Protection in Organic and Low Input Agriculture.* 239-250.

Dowdell R J, Crees R & Cannell R Q. (1983). A field study of the effects of contrasting methods of cultivation on soil nitrate content during autumn, winter and spring. *Journal of Soil Science* **34**: 367-379.

EFRC. (1997). Weed control in organic cereal crops. *Research Note 16.* Elm Farm Research Centre, Newbury.

Eisele J A & Kopke U. (1997). Choice of variety in organic farming: New criteria for winter wheat ideotypes. *Pflanzenbauwissen-schaften,* **1(1),5**. 19-24.

Fuller R J. (1997). Response of birds to organic arable farming: Mechanisms and evidence. *Proceedings of the 1997 Brighton Crop Protection Conference – Weeds.* 897-906.

Gooding M J, Cosser N D, Thomson A J, Davies W P & Froud-Williams R J. (1997). The effect of cultivar a Rht genes on the competitive ability, yield and bread-making qualities of organically grown wheat. *Proceeding 3rd ENOF Workshop, Ancona, 1997: Resource use in organic farming*, 113-1216.

Griepentrog H-W, Weiner J & Kristensen L. (2000). Increasing the suppression oif weeds by varying sowing parameters. *Proceedings 13th IFOAM Scientific Conference*, 173.

Grevsen, K (2000). Competitive ability of pea (Pisum sativum L) cultivars against weeds. *Proceedings 13th IFOAM Scientific Conference*, 179.

Grundy A C, Froud-Williams R J & Boatman N D. (1997) The control of weeds in cereals using an integrated approach. *Aspects of Applied Biology*, **50**,: *Optimising cereal inputs: Its scientific basis*, 367-374.

Hammarström L, Gillberg B & Pettersson H. (1993). Inter-row cultivation in cereals. *Communications of the Fourth Conference IFOAM – Non-Chemical Weed Control*, Dijon. Erata.

Hewson R T, Roberts H A & Bond W. (1973). Weed competition in spring-sown broad beans. *Horticultural Research* **13**: 25-32.

Jones P A, Blair A M & Orson J H. (1996). Mechanical damage to kill weeds. *Proceedings of the 1996 Second International Weed Control Congress*, Copenhagen. 949-954.

Jornsgaard B, Rasmussen K, Hill J & Christiansen J L. (1996) Influence of nitrogen on competition between cereals and their natural weed populations. *Weed Research, 1996*, 36, 461-470.

Kouwenhoven J K & Terpstra R. (1979). Sorting action of tines and tine-like tools in the field. *Journal of Agricultural Engineering Research* **24**: 95-113.

Lemerle E, Verbeek B, Cousens R D & Coombes N E. (1996) The potential for selecting wheat varities strongly competitive against weeds. *Weed Research, 36*, 505-513

Mattsson B, Nylander C & Ascard J. (1990). Comparison of seven inter-row weeders. *III Internationale Knoferenz zu Aspekten der nicht-chemischen Beikrautregulierung*, Linz 1989. 91-108.

Millington S, Stopes C E, Woodwatd L & Vogtmann H. (1990). Rotational design and the limits of organic systems – the stockless organic farm? *BCPC Monograph No.45: Crop Protection in Organic and Low Input Agriculture*. 163-173.

Mohler C L & Galford A E. (1997). Weed seedling emergence and seed survival: separating the effects of seed position and soil modification by tillage. *Weed Research* **37**: 147-156.

Organic Cereals and Pulses

Morris P J & Parrish D J. (1992) Effects of sunflower residues and tillage on winter wheat. *Field Crops Research*, **29(1992)**, 317-327.
Morrish C H. (1995). Aspects of mechanical and non-chemical weed control in forage maize. *PhD thesis, Wye College, University of London*.
Nieto J H, Brondo M A & Gonzalez J T. (1968). Critical periods of the crop growth cycle for competition from weeds. *Pest Article News Summary* **14**: 159-166.
Orson J H. (1990). Population thresholds as an aid to weed control. *British Crop Protection Council Monograph No.45*: Crop Protection in Organic and Low Input Agriculture. 41-48.
Patriquin D G, Bains D, Lewis J & Macdougall A. (1988). Weed control in organic farming systems. In: *Weed Control in Agroecosystems: Ecological Approaches*. Eds M A Altieri and M Liebman. CRS Press. 303-317.
Peruzzi A, Silvestri N, Gini N & Coli A. (1993). Weed control of winter cereals by means of weeding harrows: First experimental results. *Agricoltura Mediterranea* **123**: 236-242.
Popay A I, Daly M J, Knight T L, Stiefel W, White S & Bulls P B. (1992). Weed management without chemicals in New Zealand cereal crops. *Proceedings of the 9th IFOAM International Scientific Conference*, Brazil. 117-120.
Rasmussen J. (1990). Selectivity – an important parameter on establishing the optimum harrowing technique for weed control in growing cereals. *Proceedings of the European Weed Research Society Symposium, Integrated Weed Management in Cereals*. 144-157.
Rasmussen J. (1991). Optimising the intensity of harrowing for mechanical weed control in winter wheat. *Proceedings of the 1991 Brighton Crop Protection Conference – Weeds*. 177-184.
Rasmussen J. (1992). Testing harrows for mechanical control of weeds in agricultural crops. *Weed Research* **32**: 267-274.
Rasmussen J. (1993a). Can high densities of competitive weeds be controlled efficiently by harrowing or hoeing in agricultural crops. *Communications of the fourth International Conference IFOAM – Non-Chemical Weed Control*, Dijon. 83-88.

112

Rasmussen J. (1993b). The influence of harrowing used for post-emergence weed control on the interference between crop and weeds. *Proceedings of the European Weed Research Society Symposium, Quantitative approaches in weed and herbicide research and their practical application.* 209-217.

Rasmussen J. (1993c). Limitations and prospects for mechanical weed control. *SEC Workshop: Scientific basis for codes of good agricultural practice.* Eds V W L Jordan. 131-142.

Rasmussen J. (1995). Selective weed harrowing in cereals. *Biological Agriculture and Horticulture* **12**: 29-46.

Rasmussen J. (1996). Mechanical weed management. *Proceedings of the 1996 Second International Weed Control Congress,* Copenhagen. 943-948.

Rasmussen J & Svenningsen T. (1995). Selective weed harrowing in cereals. *Biological Agriculture and Horticulture* **12**: 29-46.

Richards M C & Davies D H K. (1991). Potential for reducing herbicide inputs/ rates with more competitive cereal cultivars. *Proceedings Brighton Crop Protection Conference – Weeds – 1991,* 1237-1240.

Roberts H A & Potter M E. (1980). Emergence patterns of weed seedlings in relation to cultivation and rainfall. *Weed Research* **20**: 377-386.

Rydberg T. (1994). Weed harrowing – the influence of driving speed and driving direction on degree of soil covering and the growth of weed and crop plants. *Biological Agriculture and Horticulture* **10**: 197-205.

Samuel A M & Guest S J. (1990). Effect of seed rate and within crop cultivation in organic winter wheat. *British Crop Protection Council Monograph No.45: Crop Protection in Organic and Low Input Agriculture.* 49-54.

Smith S P, Iles D R & Jordan V W L. (1994). Nutritional implications of mechanical intervention for weed control in integrated farming systems. *Aspects of Applied Biology 40: Arable Farming Under CAP Reform.* 403-406.

Steele J. (1997). Mechanical weed control. *New Farmers & Grower* **55**: 28-29.

Stöppler-Zimmer H. (1994). Die nicht-chemische regulierung des wildpflanzenbesatzes im ökologischen Landbau als Alternative zum Herbizideinsatz. Wissenschaftszentrum Für Sozialforschung, Berlin.

Taylor B R, Watson C A, Stockdale E A, Mckinlay R G, Younie D & Cranstoun D A S. (2001). Current practices and future prospects for organic cereal production: Survey and literature review. *HGCA Research Review No. 45*, HGCA, London.

Terpstra R & Kouwenhoven J K. (1981). Inter-row and intra-row weed control with a hoe-ridger. *Journal of Agricultural Engineering Research* **26**: 127-134.

Tillett N D & Hague T. (1999). Computer vision based hoe guidance - an initial trial. Journal of Agricultural Engineering Research **74**:225-236.

Weaver S E, Kropff S E & Groeneveld R M W. (1992). Use of ecophysiological models for crop-weed interference: The critical period of weed interference. *Weed Science* **40**: 302-307.

Welsh J P, Bulson H A J, Stopes C E, Froud-Williams R J & Murdoch A J. (1997). Mechanical weed control in organic winter wheat. *Aspects of Applied Biology* **50**: *Optimising Cereal Inputs - Its Scientific Basis.* 375-384.

Welsh J P, Bulson H A J, Stopes C E, Froud-Williams R J & Murdoch A J. (1999). The critical weed-free period in organically-grown winter wheat. *Annals of Applied Biology* **134**:315-320.

Welsh J P, Philipps L, Bulson H A J & Wolfe M. (1999). Weed control strategies for organic cereal crops. *Proceedings 1999 Brighton Crop Protection Conference – Weeds*, 945-950.

Wilson B J, Wright K J & Butler R C. (1993). The effect of different frequencies of harrowing in the autumn or spring on winter wheat and on the control of *Stellaria media* (L.) vill., *Galium aparine* and *Brassica napus*. *Weed Research* **33**: 501-506.

Younie D. (2001). Weed control in organic cereals. *Organic farming Technical Summary, SAC, OFTS6.*
www.sac.ac.uk/internal/Organic/Ofts6.pdf.

Younie D & Taylor B R. (1995). Maximising crop competition to minimise weeds. Unpublished, SAC, Aberdeen.

Chapter 6

Maintaining Grain Quality: Milling, Malting and Feed

M.F.F. CARVER[1] and B.R. TAYLOR[2]

*[1] Arable Research Centres, Manor Farm, Daglingworth,
Cirencester, Gloucestershire GL7 7AH
[2] SAC Agronomy Department, Ferguson Building, Craibstone
Estate, Bucksburn, Aberdeen AB21 9YA*

INTRODUCTION

The first question for any organic cereal grower to ask concerns the quality requirements for the intended market. For feed grain destined for home use there may be few requirements but if the crop is intended for a premium market such as milling or malting there will be stringent quality criteria, and because the processes used are the same as for conventional grain, the quality criteria are the same for organic and non-organic markets. The challenge for the organic cereal producer aiming at a premium market is to meet these stringent criteria whilst complying with the organic standards.

MILLING WHEAT

Wheat is the most important UK cereal for both organic and non-organic farmers and accounts for just over half of the organic grain production in the UK (Soil Association, 2001). Production methods for organic wheat are described below and draw on trials carried out by the Arable Research Centres (ARC), on a recent UK Home-Grown Cereals Authority (HGCA) review of organic cereal production (Taylor *et al.*, 2001), and on unpublished sources including the HGCA and the Ernest Cook Trust.

Specifications for bread-making wheat

The quality specifications for bread-making wheat for organic flour production are identical to those for conventional production but millers acknowledge that high protein contents are difficult to achieve in UK organic systems and may relax protein requirement by a percent or so. A typical specification is in Table 6.1.

Table 6.1.   Specifications for organic bread-making wheat

	Bread-making wheat
Minimum grain protein (%)	12
Minimum Hagberg falling number	250
Minimum specific weight (kg/hl)	76
Maximum screenings (2mm)	3
Maximum grain moisture (%)	15

Currently only about 10% of the UK organic flour market is supplied from home-produced organic wheat. Although organic growers find it difficult to reach the required protein standards, millers may use samples with lower protein levels for which a reduced premium is paid. Another problem is consistency of supply. Specialist organic bakers use relatively small tonnages of flour; these can be met, at a price, by specialist millers who purchase named varieties such as Maris Widgeon. However, industrial bakers require relatively large amounts of consistent quality in order to avoid constant changes to automated baking processes. This is difficult to achieve from organic farms in the UK where production units are small and there is a wide choice of varieties. To increase the uptake of UK organic wheat for bread-making, larger production units with single or few varieties are needed.

With up to 90% of organic flour produced in the UK being made from organic wheat imported from Canada, Australia, Germany and increasingly Eastern Europe, it is clear that UK organic wheat growers could have access to a much larger market if problems of quality and consistency of production could be overcome. Millers can blend flours for organic bakers and thereby dramatically increase the market for organic grain for bread-making.

Choice of variety

Yield differences among varieties intended for different markets are as pronounced under organic management as they are under non-organic management. In ARC organic variety trials harvested in 2000 and 2001 the highest yielding commercially available wheat varieties in each of the NABIM (National Association of British and Irish Millers) use groups are shown in Table 6.2.

Table 6.2.   Yield and specific weight of wheat varieties in different NABIM groups (Source: ARC).

NABIM Group*	Variety	2000		2001	
		Yield (t/ha)	Specific weight (kg/hl)	Yield (t/ha)	Specific weight (kg/hl)
1	Hereward	4.32	73.8	5.00	71.3
2	-	-	-	5.16	69.7
3	Claire	4.18	70.7	5.17	72.9
~~4~~	Deben	4.33	67.0	5.54	71.3
4	Except			5.31	
	M.Widgeon	4.00		3.96	

*1, Bread-making; 2, Potential bread-making; 3, Biscuit; 4, Feed.

There was no yield difference between feed and bread-making varieties in 2000 but a 9.7% difference in 2001. By comparison, Maris Widgeon, a popular organic milling variety, gave a similar yield to the best varieties in 2000 but was substantially lower yielding in 2001.

Establishing the crop

The first decisions to be made for any crop are source of seed and seed rate to be used. Organic seed production is addressed elsewhere (Chapter 7) but growers should not forget that, whilst seed-borne diseases are thankfully very uncommon in most seasons in the UK, they can have devastating effects when they do occur.

In the HGCA Survey (Taylor *et al.*, 2001*)* growers were asked where their seed had been sourced and how their seed rates compared to conventional rates. In 51% of crops conventional untreated seed had been used and in 75%, seed rates were above those used in conventional systems. There is a clear need for more organic cereal seed multiplication if shortages are to be avoided when the derogation on organic seed ends in December 2003.

Table 6.3.   **Effect of seed rate on estimated grain yield**
(Source: Taylor *et al.*, 2001)

Seed rate	Estimated Grain Yield (t/ha)
Below average	2.8
Average	4.4
Above average	4.3

A primary reason for using higher seed rates is to give rapid early ground cover to minimise weed problems. The survey did not suggest that higher cereal yields resulted from higher seed rates (Table 6.3). However, ARC trials in 2000 and 2001 with Maris

Widgeon suggest that seed rate has a marginal effect on specific weight and that higher seed rates should be used for organic wheat than are used in non-organic systems. Thus increasing seed rates resulted in higher specific weights in one year of the trials and higher yields in another (Table 6.4).

Table 6.4. **Effect of seed rate on yield and specific weight** (Source: ARC).

Seeds/m^2	Harvest 2000		Harvest 2001	
	Yield (t/ha)	Specific weight. (kg/hl)	Yield (t/ha)	Specific weight (kg/hl)
200	2.67	71.1	3.74	76.4
300	2.62	72.8	3.95	76.3
400	2.80	72.6	3.88	76.3
500	2.96	72.9	3.96	76.7
LSD	0.47		0.18	

Management of soil fertility

The HGCA survey showed that organic cereal growing is very dependent upon soil fertility built up during the cropping sequence plus the use of home-produced or bought-in manures (Table 6.5).

Table 6.5. **Methods of providing N fertility in cereal crops** (Source: Taylor *et al.*, 2001)

	% of cereal crops
Rotation	90
Home-produced manure	48
Green manures	12
Bought-in manures	9
Other (mainly outdoor pigs)	5

However, many growers attempt to boost the yield and quality of their cereal grain by the use of permitted inputs such as seaweed products. ARC have conducted a number of trials on 'permitted products', particularly to boost grain protein levels of milling wheat. The results of a trial on the variety Malacca, harvested in 2001, are shown in Table 6.6.

Table 6.6.   Influence of permitted products on yield and grain quality of winter wheat (cv. Malacca) in 2001 (Source: ARC)

Input	Yield (t/ha)	Specific weight (kg/hl)	Grain Protein (%)	Hagberg falling number
Untreated	5.08	70.4	9.68	251
Seaweed Extract A	4.97	71.5	10.11	359
Seaweed Extract B	5.05	71.5	9.86	327
Seaweed Extract C	5.19	72.5	10.29	348
Seaweed Extract D	4.87	70.7	10.23	289
Organic Manure	5.20	71.0	10.71	279
LSD	0.36			

Four commercially-available seaweed extracts were evaluated at their recommended application rates which in one case (Extract D) was three applications during the season of 4 litres/ha, 3 litres/ha and 3 litres/ha. They were compared to an untreated control and organic manure (a liquid cow manure formulation applied three times during the season at 4 litres/ha at each application). No treatment produced a significant yield response over the untreated but there was some indication that specific weights increased where treatments had been applied. Grain protein responses were more consistent and all the treatments increased protein levels, the organic manure treatment by 1.03%.

Crop protection

Weeds, pests, and diseases all affect the yield and quality of bread-making wheat. Weeds compete with the crop and make harvesting difficult; pests and diseases reduce photosynthesis, reduce grain filling and cause discolouration and damage to the sample. In the HGCA survey (Taylor *et al.,* 2001), four times as many organic cereal growers saw weeds as a problem than saw pests or diseases as problems.

Cereal yield responses to effective weed control are generally in the range 20 to 50%. Weed control options for organic cereal growers are discussed elsewhere (Chapter 5) and include variety choice, husbandry and mechanical weeding. In an ARC trial mechanical weeding was carried out on Maris Widgeon sown at two seed rates. Although weed levels were low in the trials and yield responses small (Table 6.7), there was an indication of increased specific weight from the control of weeds as well as from the higher seed rate.

Table 6.7.   Response of winter wheat (cv. Maris Widgeon) to mechanical weeding and seed rate (Source: ARC).

Seed Rate (seeds/m^2)	Weed Control	Yield (t/ha)	Specific weight (kg/hl)
200	None	2.67	71.1
200	Harrow comb*	2.85	73.6
400	None	2.80	72.6
400	Harrow comb*	3.08	74.0
LSD		0.47	

*one pass in March

A second trial in 2001, sown at 400 seeds/m^2, again showed some evidence of a specific weight increase following weed control (Table

6.8). Although the advantages to grain quality may be small in these trials, they indicate opportunities for growers to improve the value of their grain.

Table 6.8. **Responses to mechanical weeding in Maris Widgeon** (Source: ARC)

Weed Control	Yield (t/ha)	Spec. wt.(kg/hl)
None	4.71	74.3
Harrow comb x 1	4.85	75.1
Harrow comb x 2	4.93	75.2
LSD	0.26	

Recommendations for growing milling wheat

- Choose a variety that has a recognised end market.
- Try to avoid short-strawed varieties unless you are confident that weeds will not be a problem.
- Do not reduce seed rates (currently lower seed rates are being widely advocated in conventional cereal growing).
- Use mechanical weed control to remove weeds and possibly help to maintain/improve grain quality.

MALTING BARLEY

There is a small but growing UK demand for organic malting barley. Barley malt is used mostly for the production of organic beer, but also for making malt and grain whisky, and malt extract. UK organic malting barley production is estimated at about 800 tonnes per year (Soil Association, 2001) but this does not meet demand and some 50% of requirements are imported. The shortage of supply has kept prices, presently about £200/tonne, above conventionally-produced malting barley (Barrington *et al.*, 2001). Because of the small market and the limited number of malting barley users in the UK, growers are advised to grow the crop on contract (Lampkin and Measures, 2001).

There is no reason why good malting barley cannot be produced organically in the UK, but trials data on the agronomy of the crop is lacking. In the Czech Republic the quality of organically-produced malting barley was found to be of comparable or better quality than that from intensive and conventional systems, although quality was more affected by environment (season and site) than by growing system (Petr *et al.*, 2000).

Specifications for malting barley

Grain specifications for the organic market are the same as those for the non-organic market and are summarised in Table 6.9. In general most UK maltsters appear satisfied with the quality of the organic malting barley which they are offered. However, while grain nitrogen levels are normally acceptable, screenings and admixture are sometimes higher than from non-organic samples.

Table 6.9. **Specifications for organic malting barley**
(Source: Taylor *et al.*, 2001)

	Malting barley
Variety	Approved by IGB[*]
Grain N (%)	1.47 to 1.83
Minimum germination (%)	97
Maximum screenings (%)	
England and Wales (2.25mm)	6
Scotland (2.50mm)	10
Maximum admixture (%)	2
Maximum moisture (%)	15
Sound grain of good visual appearance and smell	

[*]Institute and Guild of Brewing

For organic malting barley, less emphasis is placed on variety than is the case with non-organic malting barley and although buyers want to know the variety they are getting, malt may be sold on specification or performance rather than by variety. Named varieties may be bought on sample and samples not meeting specification may be acceptable, especially where there is a shortage of supply and blending can be used to achieve the required quality.

Choice of variety

A good malting variety is essential to meet specifications. Traditionally, spring varieties are used in the UK for malting but in the last 10 to 15 years winter varieties have dominated the market in England. Winter varieties may be less suitable for organic growers than spring varieties: N mineralised as a result of autumn cultivations is not fully utilised by the crop; spring N is required before significant mineralisation has occurred; autumn weeding may be required when soil conditions are not suitable; and there is a risk of Barley Yellow Dwarf Virus and the development over winter of other diseases.

Current UK cereal recommended lists from NIAB, SAC, DARD and ARC include a number of varieties with malting potential, some of which have been tested in organically-managed trials. Yields and agronomic characteristics of spring and winter malting barley varieties described in the NIAB Cereals Variety Handbook (NIAB, 2000) are shown in Table 6.10. Those with approval from The Institute and Guild of Brewing are most likely to be favoured by maltsters.

At present most organic malting barley in the UK is spring-sown but there is no breeding programme aimed at producing varieties of malting barley specifically adapted to organic growing systems. Varieties recommended by The Institute and Guild of Brewing (IGB), such as Chariot and Optic, are preferred by maltsters. Chariot is earlier, taller and more resistant to mildew than Optic, but almost as susceptible to *Rhynchosporium*. Of the newer varieties, Chalice has excellent disease resistance but short straw whilst other varieties such as Cellar and Pewter, have some characteristics which suit organic conditions, but growers should ensure that they have been accepted by commercial maltsters before committing themselves.

Table 6.10. **Yields and agronomic characteristics of malting varieties from organic and untreated non-organic trials** (From NIAB, 2000).

	Yield (limited data)	Agronomic characteristics
Spring varieties		
Berwick	(Good)	Tall, early and disease resistant, but weak straw and commercially untested for malting quality
Cellar	Above average	New variety with good resistance to mildew and brown rust, but very short straw, liable to brackle.
Chalice*	Above average	Good overall disease resistance, but short straw. Malting recommendation for northern areas
Chariot*	Average	Well tried malting variety suitable for organic production though weak on Rhynchosporium.
Chime(*)	Above average	New variety with good resistance to mildew and brown rust but short straw.
Decanter*	Above average	Good resistance to mildew and yellow rust. Dual purpose variety for high DP malt.

Optic*	Poor	Popular malting variety with average straw height, late maturity and susceptibility to Rhynchosporium.
Pewter	(Good)	New variety with good resistance to mildew, Rhynchosporium and BYDV but very short straw.
Prisma*	Poor	Very susceptible to mildew and liable head loss but tall and well tried for malting.
Tavern(*)	Good	New variety, with very short straw and poor mildew resistance. Appears unsuitable for organic production.

Winter varieties

Fanfare*	Above average	Short, weak straw and susceptible to mildew. Does not appear suitable for organic production.
Leonie	(Below average)	New variety with short, strong straw and good resistance to disease apart from yellow rust.
Pearl*	Good	Tall variety with reasonable disease resistance but rather weak straw. Good yield and malting potential.
Regina*	Below average	Popular malting variety in England. Average straw height, susceptible to mildew and yellow rust.
Vanessa	(Average)	New variety, with good resistance to mildew and Rhynchosporium. No commercial malting information.

*   Approved and (*) provisionally approved for malting by the IGB for harvest 2001 for all or some UK regions.

Of the winter varieties, Pearl looks promising for organic production. It has full or provisional IGB approval as a malting variety for all regions of the UK, a high yield, good overall disease resistance, and relatively long and stiff straw. Winter barley is most likely to produce a malting sample in southern parts of the UK where late uptake of nitrogen may be restricted by lack of soil moisture.

Soils

Although malting barley can be grown on a wide variety of soil types, it is most suited to lighter, chalky or sandy soils of the relatively low-lying and drier eastern counties of the UK and in some areas of the west of England and Shropshire. Here the opportunities for early sowing and easier harvests are greatest. Light soils liable to drought can produce shrivelled grain with a high level of screenings. On the other hand, heavy soils tend to delay drilling in spring and prolong the growing period because of their moisture holding capacity. Light, sandy or chalk soils do not have large reserves of N so the likelihood of producing a sample to meet specifications is highest.

Position in rotation and management of N

The amount of soil N and the time at which it becomes available to the crop greatly influences grain N content of malting barley (McTaggart and Smith, 1995). Whilst lack of N fertility may be a problem in some organic crops (see previous section on milling wheat), in the case of malting barley it is important also to manage the timing of N availability to the crop.

In non-organic systems, spring malting barley normally follows a cereal and is sown early to maximise starch production relative to N uptake, fertiliser N applications are reduced below those for feed crops and nitrogen is applied early, so that most of the nitrogen is taken up by the time of anthesis (McTaggart and Smith, 1995). In organic systems, the crop uses mineralised soil N and N supplied in organic manures and these become available gradually during the growing season in response to cultivation and rising soil temperatures.

Previous crop influences the amount of mineralised soil N which becomes available during the growing season. There is little information about the most suitable crop to precede organic malting barley. However, soil N levels are normally highest after a grass/clover ley and lowest after exhaustive crops such as cereals; grain legumes such as peas and beans can contribute up to 40 kg/ha N to the following crop (Taylor *et al.*, 2001).

It should be possible to grow malting barley after a number of organic crops such as root crops to which organic manures have been applied, or as second cereals, when organic manures may be required before ploughing. Long-term grass/clover leys are not suitable crops before malting barley.

The timing of cultivations affects the amount of mineralised N taken up by the crop. Younie and Watson (1995) compared N uptake and grain yield of unfertilised spring barley following a grass/clover ley. Nitrogen uptake and grain yield were higher when the ley was ploughed in January than when it was ploughed in April, but grain nitrogen content was also greater (Table 6.11).

Table 6.11. The effect of date of cultivation on N uptake and yield of spring barley (Source: Younie and Watson, 1995)

Ploughing date	N uptake in July (kg/ha)	Grain yield (t/ha)	Grain N (%)
January	130.4	7.4	1.77
April	92.6	6.1	1.60

Mechanical weeding of the growing cereal crop, for example with a spring tine weeder, may encourage soil N mineralisation through disturbance of the soil. However, in several on-farm experiments with winter wheat grain N levels were not consistently or significantly altered by tine weeding (Bulson *et al.*, 1996), and in a separate trial at Elm Farm Research Centre, where grain N was increased by weeding this was attributed mainly to a decrease in competition for N from weeds.

Mechanical weeding in cereals is normally carried out before the start of stem elongation; in winter barley this will be in March or April and therefore unlikely to have a large effect on grain nitrogen. Spring barley reaches stem elongation later and harrowing at this time in warmer conditions may release more N for a crop which is in any case lower-yielding.

Crop protection

Crop protection measures are more important for malting, with its tighter specifications than for feed barley. Weeds compete for nutrients, water and light, and reduce tillering, head numbers and yield. Weed control measures have been found to have relatively small effects on grain size in winter wheat (Bulson *et al.*, 1996). Weeds make harvesting slow and difficult, delay ripening and impair sample quality through admixture. Undersowing may also cause some of these problems where the crop is not a good competitor. Weed control is dealt with fully elsewhere.

Foliar disease reduces photosynthesis and affects grain filling and the level of screenings (Conry and Dunne, 2001). The first line of defence is to choose a resistant variety and growers should select varieties with the most appropriate profile of resistance for their own situation. The spring variety Pewter and the winter variety Pearl combine moderate or good resistance to both powdery mildew and *Rhynchosporium*.

Harvesting and storage

The main risks at this stage of malting barley production are damaged grain, moulds and pest damage, and poor germination. Physical damage such as bruising and crushing may be due to faulty combine settings; splitting and skinning of the grain can be affected by combine settings but they are also affected by growing conditions and variety (Hoad *et al.*, 1999). Loss of germination, moulds and pests can be due to failure to dry and store correctly.

Other actions which growers can take include dressing, drying and cooling grain. Grain which is to be stored for any more than a few days should be dried to below 15% moisture and cooled to between $10^{o}C$ and $15^{o}C$ (HGCA, 2001). Most maltsters prefer to dry grain themselves in order to avoid any loss of germination through excessive drying temperatures.

The quality of malting barley can be improved after harvest by dressing grain to remove small grains or screenings. Since small grain has a high N content, dressing will generally reduce the grain N level of the sample.

Recommendations for growing organic malting barley

- Choose a variety approved by the IGB, competitive against weeds and resistant to local diseases.
- Do not grow as a first cereal crop after a grass/clover ley.
- If applying organic manures apply to winter crops in early in spring, to spring crops before ploughing.
- For spring crops earlier ploughing will encourage yield but may give higher grain N.
- Use mechanical weed control early to avoid a late flush of N and to remove competition.
- Grow on contract.
- Take care if drying.

FEED GRAIN

The quality specifications for feed grain are less detailed than for milling or malting. Variety is not usually specified and market requirements are based on moisture, specific weight and screenings or admixture (Table 6.12).

Table 6.12.   Specifications for organic feed grain

	Wheat	Barley	Oats
Variety	Any	Any	Any
Maximum grain moisture (%)	15	15	15
Minimum specific weight (kg/hl)	72	63.5	50
Maximum admixture (%)	-	2	2
Maximum screenings 2mm (%)	3	-	-
Bold, sound grain of good visual appearance and smell			

The growing and harvesting of cereals to produce grain with low moisture and admixture are described above. Good specific weight depends on variety and on producing a bold, uniform sample. Six-row winter barley varieties tend to have lower specific weights than 2-row varieties. Selection of a uniform fertile field, good weed control, avoidance of lodging caused by excessive seed rates, avoidance of secondary tillering caused by uneven sowing, and use of a variety with appropriate disease resistance will help produce bold grain with a good specific weight. Correct combine settings and dressing the grain to ensure that awns and admixture are removed will also help.

As for premium markets, the markets for feed grain are also under supplied and grain is being purchased from overseas to produce organic feed for UK livestock. It is surely unacceptable in the longer term to have to transport organic grain halfway around the world to produce organic feed for livestock and bread for human consumption.

Like millers and maltsters, compounders will increasingly demand larger, more homogeneous batches of grain. Maintaining quality for all these markets will be an on-going challenge for all organic cereal producers.

REFERENCES

Barrington L., Stocker P., Haward R. and Yeats B. (2001). Eye on the market. *Organic Farming*, 70, 10.

Bulson, H., Welsh, J., Stopes, C. and Woodward, L. (1996). *Weed Control in Organic Cereal Crops*. Final Report of EU contract AIR-CT93-0852, Elm Farm Research Centre.

Conry, M.J. and Dunne, B. (2001). Influence of number and timing of fungicide applications on the yield and quality of early and later-sown spring malting barley grown in the south-east of Ireland. *J. agric. Sci., Cambs.*, 136, 159-167.

HGCA (2001). *Introductory Guide to Malting Barley*. Home-Grown Cereals Authority, London.

Hoad, S., Cochrane, P., Cranstoun, D., Ellis, R., Thomas, B., Rajasekeran, P. and South, J. (1999). Grain splitting in barley. HGCA Agronomy Roadshows '99, HGCA, London.

Lampkin, N. and Measures, M. (2001). *2001 Organic Farm Management Handbook*. University of Wales, Aberystwyth, and Elm Farm Research Centre, Newbury.

McTaggart, I.P. and Smith, K.A. (1995). The effect of rate, form and timing of fertilizer N on nitrogen uptake and grain N content in spring malting barley. *J. agric. Sci., Cambs.*, 125, 341-353.

NIAB (2000). *Cereal Variety Handbook*. National Institute of Agricultural Botany, Cambridge.

Petr, J., Skerik, J., Psota, V. and Langer, I. (2000). Quality of malting barley grown under different cultivation systems. *Monatsschrift-fur-Brauwissenschaft*, 53, 90-94.

Soil Association (2001). *The Organic Food and Farming Report 2000*. The Soil Association, Bristol.

Taylor, B.R., Watson, C.W., Stockdale,E.A., McKinlay, R.G., Younie, D. and Cranstoun, D.A.S. (2001). *Current practices and Future Prospects for Organic Cereal Production: Survey and Literature Review*. Research Review No. 45, HGCA, London.

Younie, D. and Watson, C.A. (1995). Crop growth and nitrogen recovery following ploughing of grass/clover swards. In *Grassland into the 21st Century: Challenges and Opportunirties* (Ed. E.G. Pollott) Occasional Symposium, British Grassland Society, No. 30, 206-208.

Chapter 7

Producing High Quality Seed

J. E. THOMAS[1] and R. WYARTT[2]

[1]NIAB, Huntingdon Road, Cambridge CB3 OLE
[2]Wyartt Seeds Ltd., Stone Cottage, Beyton, Bury St Edmunds,
IP30 9AF

INTRODUCTION

The use of seed with germination, health, purity and vigour
characteristics appropriate to the situation in which it is sown is as
essential to organic systems as it is to conventional agriculture.
Without seed of high quality, the benefits of rotational planning,
careful variety choice, and good husbandry practice in maintaining
productive organic systems are unlikely to be realised. Seed is a
critical input, and the requirement for organically-produced seed
must not result in any acceptance of inappropriate seed quality
standards. For many seed characteristics, there should not be any
significant problems in achieving required standards under organic
production. However, for some characteristics, and in particular the
level of seed-borne diseases, there is potential for serious problems
to arise. This paper considers seed quality characteristics in cereals
and pulses, the standards to be attained, where difficulties may be
encountered, and what future measures organic seed producers and
organic growers may need to combat these.

CERTIFIED SEED AND FARM PROCESSED SEED

Standards for the production of Certified Seed of cereals and pulse
crops are governed by the UK Seed Regulations. Various aspects
of quality are included in the regulations, and organically-produced

seed will have to meet exactly the same standards before it can be sold. Farm processed seed is not subject to any statutory quality regulations, but growers may check voluntarily for one or more quality characteristics. Regardless of whether organic seed is certified or farm processed, it must itself have been grown organically in order for the ware crop produced from it to be classified as organic. Thus if an organic cereal seed grower grows untreated but conventionally-produced certified seed of the first generation (C1) on organic land, the produce from that crop would be second generation certified seed (C2) if the appropriate standards were met, and this could be sold as seed to produce an organic ware crop. Seed saved from the ware crop would also be organic seed. However, if the produce from the initial C1 generation did not meet the seed certification standards for C2 for any reason, it could not be classified as an organic grain crop.

ORGANIC SEED - A MERCHANT'S VIEW

Before the technical aspects of organic seed production are considered, some points of a more political nature need to be dealt with. Firstly, without absolute control of the derogation system, which is not apparent so far in UK, there will not be an organic seed production industry. Secondly, there are no insuperable problems to producing the five cereal and various pulse species commonly grown in the UK by organic means to meet the statutory standards which apply to all certified seed. Following from this, it is clear that there is no need for a further derogation to allow the use of conventionally-produced seed when the current one comes to an end in December 2003.

Organic farmers need to factor in the increased cost of organically-produced seed to their budgets. If this fact is not accepted now, the valuable credibility that organic farming currently enjoys could be lost. Finally, it needs to be recognised that things are more difficult in the small seeded sector, but it is possible for instance to grow clover seed in the south east of England (Kent Wild White production continues today). Grass seed production is a problem without the possibility of using large quantities of instant nitrogen, but even so, continental growers are being successful.

Clean, healthy seed of known pedigree is essential to a successful crop. It is possible to achieve the correct standards with farm saving, though for a merchant to give advice on how to do this may well mean helping organic farmers to avoid buying his product. However, it may also mean that more organic farmers can become successful seed growers, supplying the certified seed market.

Many farmers do save their own seed in the belief that they are saving money, and some organic farmers also believe that by retaining seed on the same farm for many years, the material will adapt to its local environment, and improve in performance. The rights and wrongs of these beliefs will not be argued here, but anyone producing seed needs to pay careful attention to basic technical rules and vigilance over seed-borne disease. Without such attention, farm-saving of seed under true organic conditions is a route to disaster – principally due to the characteristics of some seed-borne diseases, which can ruin a crop even though they are frequently not seen until it is too late.

Farm-savers need to follow the practice of professional seed growers to avoid these problems. Early generation, re-cleaned seed, tested for diseases, and planted in a clean field after a non-cereal crop is needed for cereal seed production. In the case of peas, a five-year break from preceding pea crops is needed.

For cereals, a clean field means avoiding couch, knotgrass and blackgrass, which compete with the crop and prevent good growth. Wild oats remain a major concern. Few fields are free of this weed, but several have manageable populations i.e. they can be rogued by the farmer. Populations need to be lower for oat seed production, since the wild species can easily be missed in an oat crop. In tall crops such as rye and triticale, the task is even harder.

Most annual weeds can be removed by harrowing or hoeing, though the weather window for doing this can be short. Wild oats, fat hen and poppy then emerge. The last two are less serious, but roguing must be carried out to remove the wild oats. From experience, it is only possible to remove about 90% of the plants in one visit – from a population of, say 1000 plants, 900 can be taken out on the first visit, 90 of the remaining 100 on a second visit, leaving 10 for a final visit.

Once the wild oat population has been managed, harvest provides the next hurdle. Will the combining be done by a contractor, how conscientious is the driver, and will he carry out instructions? Is the vacuum cleaning system powerful, and how much of a hurry is the driver in? Are the trailers and storage facilities clean? Modern intakes, pre-cleaners, driers and storage bin systems give endless possibilities for contamination, and it is advisable to use the simplest system possible. Tipping straight from the trailer onto a ventilated floor where the seed can remain until needed is ideal, but the person driving the combine is a critical factor. The amount of grain collected when a combine is cleaned properly is a reminder of what could happen – imagine it spread through 10 to 20 tonnes of seed of a new variety!

Once harvested, does the seed need cleaning – short pieces of straw may be present, perhaps some thistle or poppy heads? Mobile cleaners can be brought in, but they add cost. At this stage, the grower needs to decide how much is needed for planting (remember this seed cannot be sold), then sample it, and have disease and germination tests done before spending money on cleaning. Any wild oat seeds should be visible in the sample, as should ergots. Ergots have become a regular problem. Infection by air-borne spores is favoured by cool, damp summers when flowering takes place over a long period of time, giving a prolonged risk period. The amount of wild grasses on organic farms is increasing, in field margins and in new woodland planted into grasses which continue to flower every year. Wild grasses will maintain ergot, and it is likely to become an increasing problem not only for seed growers but organic grain producers as well.

Turning to pulse crops, these need to be started in clean fields, sown on wide rows which are hoed two or three times early in the season. A good crop canopy should develop to smother late developing weeds, though peas usually develop some weed population as they approach maturity. Wild oats are less of a problem in pulse crops, thistle heads will blow out, and cleaning on-farm is relatively easy. Seed-borne diseases are a problem, and effective sampling and then testing is essential. Germination, *Ascochyta* diseases, and stem eelworm (the latter for field beans) should be checked, and costs can mount up.

Producing high quality seed on farm needs a dedicated approach, and unless a grower is prepared to do considerable extra work without counting the cost, the end result will rarely be justified in cost terms alone. In conventional agriculture, farm saving is becoming less attractive following the introduction of the farm-saved seed royalty, which also applies to organic seed. Organic farmers have no option but to bear the costs of health tests, possibly on a relatively small amount of seed, which conventional growers can avoid by using seed treatment. Merchants producing and selling organic seed can be competitive because testing costs are spread over a much larger tonnage of seed.

QUALITY AND DISEASE ISSUES IN ORGANIC SEED

Germination, purity and vigour

Germination may be defined as the ability of a seed to produce a normal seedling. Various factors during the production and subsequent handling of seed may affect its capacity to produce a normal seedling. Such factors might include heat or mechanical damage, though these problems are rare, and are as likely to occur with conventional seed as organic seed. Purity relates both to weed seed contamination and varietal purity. Effective rotational practice, and the weed control measures described so far are essential to achieve a pure seed sample for successful production of high quality crops. Vigour describes the performance of a seed during germination and growth. Low vigour seeds are less able to produce a plant under adverse field conditions than seeds with higher vigour. Standards are not part of the certification regulations, and poor vigour is not normally a significant problem in cereal seed, though it is an important characteristic of pea seeds, especially for early sowing, and to enable the rapid growth which will help to avoid the effects of soil-borne damping off.

Disease

Seed-borne disease is perhaps the most critical aspect of organic seed production. The diseases involved fall into two categories: those which increase with successive generations of seed multiplication, and those which develop during the growing season, and are usually weather dependent. In cereals, the most important example of the latter is *Microdochium nivale*, the cause of seedling blight in wheat, barley and oats. The fungus infects the developing seed during anthesis, and without ear wash sprays, levels on seed can be very high in wet years. They may be severe enough to reduce the germination of seed, potentially to a level below the certification standard of 85%. In the absence of an effective, organically-acceptable method of controlling infection by *M. nivale* in the field during anthesis, or a seed treatment, there could be years when the supply of certified organic seed is limited, and when it will be inadvisable to use farm-saved seed. Infection might be reduced to some extent by locating seed production crops away from known wet or low-lying areas on the farm.

Winter wheat and winter oats are particularly prone to damage by seedling blight, and late sown crops will be more vulnerable than earlier ones. Increasing the seed rate can compensate to some extent, but seed with more than 5% infection should be avoided for late sowing. For earlier sowing into a good seedbed, levels up to

15% may be tolerable. Current work with *M. nivale* on conventional seed (Cockerell *et al.*, 2001) should provide information on safe thresholds for using untreated seed in a range of situations, and this will provide some guidance for organic systems. Seed-borne Septoria on wheat (*Stagonospora nodorum*) may also affect germination, and though levels on wheat crops are currently low, future shifts in the importance of this disease cannot be ruled out.

Table 7.1. **The development of seed-borne diseases**
(successive generations sown untreated)

	% seeds infected with leaf stripe	% plants infected with loose smut	% plants infected with bunt
Year 1	0.01	0.3	0.01
Year 2	0.6	1.8	0.2
Year 3	36	10.8	25

Source: Paveley *et al.*, 1996

For those diseases which increase with seed generations, conventional growers have relied on the almost universal application of seed treatments at all stages of multiplication, including the generation used for ware production. The capacity for these pathogens to increase is illustrated in Table 7.1. In the case of bunt (*Tilletia tritici*) on wheat, it is possible to harvest a crop with no noticeable bunt problem (1 in 10,000 ears infected), and see complete loss of a wheat crop (2 in 1000 ears infected) sown with untreated seed saved from it. The major seed-borne diseases of barley; leaf stripe (*Pyrenophora graminea*) and loose smut, are less catastrophic in nature, though levels can build up quickly, with one infected plant resulting in about 1% yield loss. For all three diseases, risks are also created for neighbouring crops *via* wind- blown spores, and the potential to save seed from these will decrease.

While a small number of conventional growers are health testing seed and using a treatment according to need strategy (Cockerell *et al.*, 2001), this is limited to one generation of untreated seed. The consequences of moving to two untreated generations for organic seed production are unknown. Careful monitoring and conscientious testing of the health of organic seed stocks is going to be necessary. Safe usage thresholds for different generations of seed multiplication also need to be defined.

At present it is probably advisable to take a cautious approach, and some suggested standards are shown in Table 7.2, though whether these can be achieved routinely without discarding an unacceptable number of stocks is as yet unknown. It is also possible that hitherto very rare diseases, such as covered smut on barley (*Ustilago hordei*) may increase.

Organic seed treatments and methods of disinfecting cereal seed, are already being developed (Nielsen *et al.*, 2000), and it is likely that these will be needed on some stocks, whether farm-saved or certified, both to avoid the loss of valuable multiplication seed and to maintain the supply of seed for ware production. At present, the organic grower can rely on the benefits of conventional seed treatment in early generations of cereal seed. The eventual introduction of organically-bred varieties, from breeders' nursery to C2 seed, will probably require a combination of control approaches (resistant varieties, seed health testing, and organic seed treatments) to limit the generational increase of seed-borne disease.

The concept that organic soils will have biotic and abiotic factors, which will suppress the transmission of seed-borne diseases is an attractive one, but remains largely untested. The threat from diseases such as bunt is too great to rely on this without a comprehensive research effort.

Table 7.2.   **Suggested standards for major seed-borne diseases in organic cereal seed production**

	First generation untreated	Second generation untreated
Bunt (wheat)	Nil	1 spore per seed
Loose smut (wheat and barley	0.2%	0.2%
Loose smut (oats)	100 spores per g seed	200 spores per g seed
Pyrenophora leaf stripe (barley)	Nil	2%
Pyrenophora leaf blight (oats)	Nil	2%
Microdochium (wheat and oats)	5 to 15%, depending on conditions	5 to 15%, depending on conditions

The major pulse crops, field pea and field bean, may be severely infected by leaf and pod spotting pathogens during the growing season when wet weather occurs during flowering. Infections penetrate the pod wall, leading to seed-borne disease. Infected seed can die shortly after emergence, or survive and contribute a source of inoculum for the new crop. In conventional systems, sprays are applied to prevent infection reaching the pods and seed. For field beans, there are also standards within the certification scheme for *Ascochyta fabae*, and these have contributed towards suppressing levels of the disease in the field. Farm savers should aim to achieve at least the equivalent of the C2 marketing standard for *Ascochyta fabae*, i.e. not more than 1% infection. For field peas, there are no equivalent standards for either of the two relevant pathogens on this crop (*Mycosphaerella pinodes* and *Ascochyta pisi*). However, voluntary standards may be applied, and in general any seed with more than 5% infection receives a seed treatment, and in organic seed, a 5% safe use threshold is probably appropriate.

It may be difficult to achieve both these standards, particularly in wet years, yet control of leaf and pod spotting pathogens is essential for good establishment and healthy crop development. For winter beans, it is probably advisable to use resistant varieties wherever possible, since there is evidence to indicate that seed-borne infection levels tend to be lower on these. However, in spring beans, there is little available information on *Ascochyta* resistance and there are only partial levels of resistance to *M. pinodes* in peas. It may prove necessary to confine seed production to the drier regions of the UK, and to develop organic sprays and seed treatments which can be used if these diseases occur. Grey mould (*Botrytis cinerea*) on pea pods may also affect seed quality in wet conditions. Affected seeds are chalky white in colour, and germination is reduced.

Stem nematode (*Ditylenchus dipsaci*) is seed-borne in field beans. It can affect both winter and spring varieties, and increases in wet years. There are two races of the pest, the oat-onion and giant race. The oat-onion race has a wide host range, including many weed species, as well as oats and rye, while the giant race is confined to field and broad beans. Though there are no chemical means of controlling this pest, and it has been a considerable problem in conventional production, it does have specific implications for organic production. Rotations of oats or rye and field beans may be more common in organic systems, and this could lead to a build up of soil-borne populations of the nematode which would severely limit future rotational choices. The tolerance of low-level weed populations in organic fields could also maintain populations, and it is essential not to introduce this pest *via* bean seed. Wide rotations between bean crops used for seed production are advisable, probably at least five years, with either wheat or barley.

Seed sampling for detection of disease

The distribution of fungal seed-borne diseases within a seed bulk may not be uniform, and sampling needs to be sufficiently comprehensive to ensure that any "hotspots" within the bulk can be detected. Work with *M. nivale* (Thomas *et al.*, 2001) has indicated that this disease is fairly uniformly distributed in wheat seed bulks. In the case of bunt, a severely infected, and relatively small, pocket of infected seed was detected in a 30-tonne bulk by taking 40 primary samples at random, combining these, and dividing down until a test sample was prepared.

CONCLUSIONS

Producing organic seed on farm requires a professional seed grower's approach, with additional attention to managing seed-borne disease problems, including the use of efficient sampling methods. Growers who purchase organic C2 cereal seed and save from the crop, will then be using a third generation of untreated seed, and the consequences of this in terms of the severity of diseases such as bunt are as yet unknown. Returning to bought-in C2 seed is probably a safer option. If organic certification authorities were to permit growers without a seed contract to set aside part of their land to produce their own organic seed from untreated but conventionally-produced material, the end result will then have been through two untreated generations, and growers must bear the costs of sampling and checking seed health and quality. It is highly likely that, as in other countries, the further development of organic seed treatments, resistant varieties, and cultural strategies to combat seed-borne disease will be necessary.

REFERENCES

Cockerell V, Mulholland V, McEwan M, Paveley N D, Clark W S, Anthony S, Thomas J E, Bates J, Kenyon D M and Taylor E J A, 2001. Seed treatment according to need in winter wheat. *BCPC Symposium Proceedings* No. 76, *Seed Treatment: Challenges and Opportunities* pp 111-116,
Nielsen B J, Borgen A, Kristensen L, 2000. Control of seed-borne diseases in production of organic cereals. *Proceedings of the Brighton Crop Protection Conference*, pp 171-176.

Paveley N D, Rennie W J, Reeves J C, Wray M W, Slawson D D, Clark W S, Cockerell V, and Mitchell A G (1996). Cereal Seed Health and Seed Treatment Strategies. *Home Grown Cereals Authority Research Review No 34*, Home Grown Cereals Authority, London.

Thomas J E, Smith M J, Thompson P S, Kenyon D M and Cockerell V, 2001. Requirements for effective seed sampling in the application of treatment according to need strategies. *BCPC Symposium Proceedings* No. 76, *Seed Treatment: Challenges and Opportunities* pp 167-172.

Chapter 8

Commercial Farm Case Studies: Cereals

J. M. SHARMAN[1] and R. STEELE O.B.E.[2]
[1]East Cannahars, Whitecairns, Aberdeen
[2]Chapel Farm, Netherton, Pershore, Worcestershire

COMMERCIAL FARM CASE STUDY 1:

EAST CANNAHARS, ABERDEENSHIRE, SCOTLAND

Farm Profile

The conversion of East Cannahars to organic production was started when the Sharman family moved there in 1986. The most fundamental principle of organic farming is that each enterprise complements and supports the other enterprises. In other words, every organic farm is a carefully balanced unit, in which the raising of livestock is dependent on the arable crops by way of the production of feed and straw, just as the arable enterprise is dependent on the farmyard manure (FYM) from the livestock. Neither the arable nor the livestock venture can be run in isolation.

East Cannahars is situated 10 miles north of Aberdeen on the edge of the Buchan Plain, at an altitude of about 90 metres and an annual rainfall of 750 mm. Exposure to wind and sea are notable climatic features. East Cannahars is owned, and consists of 73 hectares, of which 61 ha are ploughable and the rest permanent grass. In addition, two small neighbouring holdings are rented; a 20 ha holding, the majority of which can be ploughed and carry a rotation, and a 14 ha holding of permanent grass, just completing its second year of conversion. Both of the rented units and just over half of East Cannahars are classified as Less Favoured Areas (LFA). Much of the arable land is a light sandy loam (Macaulay Grade 3.2) with only a couple of patches of heavier soil, making it not too difficult to manage. The permanent grass includes peaty and poorer stony soils. Taking these factors together - the northerly location, the soil type and personal preferences - the heart of the farm is the herd of 40 Aberdeen Angus suckler cows, and the flock of 165 ewes. Although all the livestock are an integral part of the organic regime, until recently neither the finished cattle, nor the prime lambs were sold as organic meat, because of a lack of infrastructure for the processing of organic meat. However, with the recent expansion of the organic meat market, all livestock born after February 2000 are to be marketed under the Soil Association Symbol. Until recently, selling the stock conventionally meant that the cereals could be sold as a cash crop.

The Rotation

The farm is run on a slightly modified version of the traditional North East six-year crop rotation (three years grass followed by three years arable crops). At East Cannahars all fields, with the exception of those in permanent grass, are managed according to a 12-year cycle as follows:

Yr1 →	Yr2 →	Y3 →	Yr 4 →	Yr5 →	Yr6 →	Yr7 →	Yr8 →	Yr9 →	Y10 →	Y11 →	Y12 →
G/C	G/C	G/C	SO	Roots	SBus	G/C	G/C	G/C	G/C	SO	SBus

G/C: Grass/white clover
SO: Spring Oats
SBus: Spring barley undersown
Roots: Potatoes or swedes

This rotation ensures that the potato crop is only ever grown once every twelve years in any particular field. Composted manure is spread three times over this twelve-year cycle: on all second year grass (grown for silage) and on the land for growing potatoes. The grass gets about 25 tonnes of FYM per ha and the potatoes 50 t/ha.

Varieties and cultivation

Ploughing, at about 20cm depth, does not get under way until at least February, since leaving the land bare for a long period over winter increases the risk of erosion and nitrate leaching. The farm is located in the Nitrate-Sensitive Area of the Ythan estuary, but apart from this consideration, leaching of N also means the loss of hard-won fertility. The other reason for ploughing late is that the sheep flock is held on the final year of each ley so as not to poach the rest of the grassland. This situation has been relieved somewhat by the building of a new shed to allow the sheep to be housed for 4 to 6 weeks before lambing in April.

Early versus late ploughing has been studied by SAC, and results suggest that ploughing of leys in January is most beneficial to crop yields. This is not always possible at East Cannahars due to the weather and other factors mentioned above. Prior to sowing every crop of oats, up to 375 kg of rock phosphate are applied per hectare.

Secondary cultivations consist of discing and then a pass of a "Hays" leveller. A one-pass seeder has been used on occasions for sowing oats, to speed up the operation, but earlier machines did not appear to give a very firm seed bed especially when undersowing the cereal crop with a grass/clover mix. Designs have changed for the better now, but a concern exists that it is a very heavy machine, which means a risk of soil compaction. The oat crop should ideally be sown at the end of March or early April, otherwise the harvest is delayed. Naturally, the weather is the single most decisive factor in securing a clean, saleable sample.

The varieties which have been used at East Cannahars are Dula and Valiant. Both these varieties are tall-strawed and thus useful for weed competition and straw yield. Short-strawed varieties can suffer more from weeds but might be acceptable if one was undersowing the oats with grass. The reason for changing from Dula to Valiant was that Dula seemed to be very prone to mildew and as a result produced grain of very low specific weight, giving samples between 46 and 50 kg per hectolitre. The change to Valiant in the early nineties has led to some very successful crops.

The barley crop is best sown by about mid-April. As this crop is undersown with a grass/clover mix, more warmth in the soil produces a quicker establishment, and so enables the undersown crop to compete with weeds. Since barley ripens and is harvested earlier than oats, it gives the undersown grass and clover a better chance to establish. The variety Chariot has been used until now because the objective has been the malting market.

A 13-cm row drill is used, with oats being sown at 290 kg/ha, allowing some for the crows, who are very attracted to the untreated seed and seem to land in the field even before sowing has commenced! Barley is sown at 315 kg/ha, which is a relatively high seed rate, again allowing some for the crows but also to ensure a reasonable plant population and good competition against weeds, as tillering is limited as a consequence of the reduced fertility, with this being the last crop in the rotation.

Weeds, pests and diseases

During the growing period weeds, pests and diseases must be considered but there are few actions that can be taken. Previous actions and decisions will reduce their negative effects. Weeds are very much reduced in the first crop after the grass ley. In this respect the rotation has a positive impact. Weed growth is also restricted by the tall oat crop. Each field is different in that specific weeds may occur more abundantly in some fields than others.

Deadnettle, fumitory and charlock are the most common on East Cannahars. No form of mechanical weed control is used in cereals although it could have a beneficial effect on fields with specific problems such as charlock. This system of having no active weed control, allowing such weeds that establish to flower and set seed, does cause some concern that the weed seed bank is increasing, creating a bigger weed problem in the future. However, the presence of seven years of grass ley in the rotation will have a negative effect on seed viability in many weeds.

Perennial weeds can also be a problem, docks in particular. Docks are hand-rogued out of the cereal crop before seeds are shed in order to minimise building up the weed seedbank. If at all possible the entire dock plant is pulled out, roots included, to reduce the population of established plants. Wild oats, which are not a major problem, can also be removed at the same time as the docks so as to prevent spread and to allow some of the grain to be used for seed.

There has been one situation in which a serious invasion of docks, caused by spread from a neighbour's field, could not be controlled by hand roguing in the oat crop. After the oats and prior to the following cereal crop, the field was cultivated after ploughing, in order to loosen the dock roots. The field was ridged and run through with a two row potato digger. The dock roots were then harvested by the potato harvesting team and the majority of dock plants in the field removed.

Spear thistle is a much smaller nuisance. They do not cause a problem in cereals but rather in first year grass. Unfortunately, sheep do not eat them. Finally, couch grass (*Agropyron repens*) can manifest itself as a problem quite quickly, and although it can be tackled by cultivation methods, a big infestation should ideally be dealt with prior to conversion.

Leatherjackets are a potential threat as so much grass is ploughed during the rotation, but although mild invasions may occur at East

Cannahars from time to time, they have never been a major problem. The reason why serious invasions of leatherjackets do not occur may be related to the fact that the grass leys are relatively short-term and the final year of each grass ley is always grazed hard down by sheep in August and September, when the crane flies are searching for long grass in which to lay eggs.

Crows are another potential pest, seeming to have a sixth sense as to where oats are being sown. They do consume a certain amount of the seed sown especially behind a drill, as all they have to do is follow the line of seed. Therefore broadcasting may have an advantage over the drill in this respect. One can also hope that others are sowing at the same time but if one is the last in the area the field can look quite black! Near to harvest, if and when the oat crop lodges, crows can cause major yield reductions.

Even with less dense organic crops, fungal leaf diseases can attack the crop. The main problem at East Cannahars is mildew in both oats and barley, although barley does also suffer from other diseases. The critical factor is how quickly the flag leaf succumbs, the ability to photosynthesise is diminished, with a resulting poor grain fill. Susceptibility to mildew was the main reason for changing oat variety from Dula to Valiant. Choice of variety must be under constant review in order to ensure that the variety with greatest resistance to the prevalent diseases is grown - no active disease control measures are applied to cereal crops at East Cannahars.

With barley, and in particular the variety Chariot, there are other diseases which cause the destruction of the leaf and so reduce the chances of good grain fill (*Rynchosporium* and *Ramularia*). Since the barley is now more likely to be used at home for animal feed than sold for malting, a change of variety is called for. Finally, it has often been observed that stray barley plants growing in the oat crop can be very green and totally free from disease. This observation might point towards the possibility of growing cereal mixtures.

Harvest and yields

For grain drying, tray dryers have been used in the past, but now the grain drying is contracted to a neighbour who has a mobile gas-fired dryer. There is a screen in the dryer, which lets the seconds and harvested weed seeds be collected separately. This has two advantages:

a) The screen gives a much better sample if the grain is to be sold, and

b) Many of the weed seeds can be hammer milled, so destroying them, and they can then be fed to livestock.

On-floor storage is used and any grain to be sold off the farm is usually moved by December.

Cereal yields vary considerably from season to season. The target yield is 3.8 tonnes/hectare for both oats and barley. With oats, yields have ranged from 2.8 t/ha to 5.6 t/ha. Barley yields are generally lower because it is the second successive cereal crop in the East Cannahars rotation, does not receive farmyard manure, and is undersown with the grass/clover seed mixture. A typical yield is 2.5 t/ha, which whilst not a particularly good grain yield, can still give a reasonably satisfactory gross margin if sold for malting, and almost invariably results in a very good grass and clover establishment.

In this system, straw is an important part of the cereal enterprise, either for feed or for bedding. A substantial number of bales of conventional straw are bought-in from local farms for bedding, as insufficient is produced at East Cannahars. This is partly due to the fact that the grassy barley straw is wrapped and used for feeding as harvesting is often late and the weather is not kind enough to dry the grassy straw. It is vital that the new grass sward underneath is not damaged in a vain attempt to dry and bale straw in difficult autumn weather conditions.

Marketing and Gross Margins

With oats a milling sample is usually produced and, in the last few years, has been sold to Grampian Oat Products near Banff, part of the Morning Foods company. Problems occur when there is a long, wet autumn and the grain germinates in the head. Feeding the grain is then the only option.

The oat millers are looking for a specific weight of over 50 kg/hl. Usually specific weights in the low fifties can be achieved. In the year 2000, which was not a particularly good growing year, the milling sample had a specific weight of 54 kg/hl.

The sale prices obtained in the last three years were £150, £195 and £175 per tonne in 1998, 1999 and 2000, respectively.

Nitrogen level is the critical factor with malting barley although specific weight also needs to be satisfactory. Grain N has been as low as 1.4% but more usually it is nearer 1.5%. These figures include crops following potatoes, which might be expected to have a relatively high N content. Except perhaps for grass/clover leys, the previous crop probably has no greater influence on grain N than variation in seasonal growing conditions. Prices for malting barley samples from East Cannahars have usually been around £175 to £180 per tonne.

With organic standards now requiring the use of organically-grown seed, some of the grain is retained for seed in the following season. The grain dryer being used can dry at 50% of the usual temperature and so grain for seed is dried at this lower temperature. This is also useful for malting barley. Seed grain is then kept separate and cleaned by a mobile seed dresser. The main issues here pertain to keeping seed-borne diseases to a minimum and keeping wild oats at bay.

Tables 8.1 and 8.2 show gross margins for typical grain crops at East Cannahars. These gross margins compare with typical values for conventionally-grown cereals, at a yield level of 5.5 t/ha, of approximately £500/ha. Given that all sowing, combining and drying of grain at East Cannahars is contracted, these costs could also be reasonably be added to the gross margin analysis. This would reduce the margins at East Cannahars to £700 and £519/ha for oats and barley respectively.

Table 8.1.   Typical gross margin for milling oats at East Cannahars

			£/tonne	£/ha	
Output					
	Grain	3.8t/ha	175	665	
	Straw	2.5t/ha	35	88	
	Arable Area Payment	£209/ha		209	
	Total output				962
Variable costs					
	Seed*	290kg/ha	200	58	
	Rock phosphate	375kg/ha	120	45	
	Total variable costs				103
Gross Margin (£/ha)					859

*home-saved

Table 8.2.   Typical gross margin for malting barley at East Cannahars

			£/tonne	£/ha	
Output					
	Grain	2.8t/ha	175	438	
	Straw	1.5t/ha	35	53	
Arable Area Payment		£209/ha		209	
Total output				700	
Variable costs					
	Seed*	315kg/ha	200	63	
Total variable costs					63
Gross Margin (£/ha)					637

*Home-saved

Future developments

There are a number of alternative grain crops that do not fit the East Cannahars farming system, or which would not grow well in this system. Essentially these are the winter cereal varieties, but at East Cannahars the livestock enterprises have precedence over cereals and the grass is needed during the autumn and winter. Winter oats would produce better yields than spring oats (about 5 to 5.5 t/ha), as well as an abundance of straw, and harvesting would be earlier. Triticale is another possibility, with a good level of grain protein and very competitive against weeds.

Winter barley and winter wheat would be difficult to grow organically in this area. Winter barley is a very heavy feeder so is not really suited to an organic system. With winter wheat, the season is not really long enough and this can bring harvesting problems, making it a risky crop.

Sourcing high-protein animal feeds for the organic farmer is quite difficult, and with the disappearance in 2005 of the derogation to allow 10% of feed from conventional sources, lupins may provide a means of producing a traceable, high protein feed on farm. However, they do not attract Arable Area Payment in Scotland, and in any case considerable research still needs to be carried out to assess whether they can be grown and (more especially) harvested successfully under organic conditions in the North of Scotland. However, there are further options to produce high-protein feeds, either in the form of pea silage, or peas and beans as a pulse crop, and indeed in the form of mixtures with cereals.

Mixtures of cereals themselves also may have considerable potential. Obviously such a crop could only be used for feeding, but disease levels should be reduced, leading to better yields. Different ripening times may be a potential problem area.

This paper has described how one farmer grows cereals in an organic regime in northern Britain. The approach at East Cannahars is to use spring cereals, which complement the enterprise mix on the farm. Good, timely sowing to achieve a speedy germination and ground cover to counteract weed pressure is essential. This technique of "shutting the gate" from sowing until harvest (except for some roguing of perennial weeds), may not suit every farmer, and it does cause some concern about building up the weed seed bank in the soil.

Finally, although this conference has focussed specifically on grain crops, it is important to emphasise again that all the enterprises on an organic farm work together to create a whole organism, and that in practice none of these can really be dealt with in isolation without taking the whole farm picture into account.

COMMERCIAL FARM CASE STUDY 2:

CHAPEL FARM, NETHERTON, PERSHORE, WORCESTERSHIRE

Farm Profile

Chapel Farm is 338 hectares in size of which 317 hectares (all eligible for Arable Area Payments) are in arable rotation. The altitude of the farm ranges from 30 to 61 metres above sea level. Average annual rainfall is 600 mm. Rainfall has been recorded for thirty-six years and the last three calendar years have been much wetter than average, with the year 2000 and the spring of 2001 being the wettest of all.

Soil types on the farm are Lias Clay with Kemper Marl and Badsey Loam. Soil pH levels are relatively high and lime is seldom required. Soil phosphate levels are generally low but potash is adequate except on parts of Badsey Loam. Conversion of the farm to organic production began in 1984 and the whole farm had been converted by 1997.

Crop rotations

Two rotations are followed at Chapel Farm:

Rotation 1; with grass/white clover leys primarily for grazing

Yr1 →	Yr2 →	Yr3 →	Yr4 →	Yr5 →	Y6 →
G/WC	G/WC	G/WC	WW	WW or SW	WO

Rotation 2; with grass/red clover leys primarily for silage

Yr1 →	Yr2 →	Yr3 →	Yr4 →
G/RC	G/RC	WW	WO

G/WC: Grass/white clover   WW: Winter wheat
G/RC: Grass/red clover   SW;   Spring wheat
                                  WO: Winter Oats

At least half the rotation has to be a legume – usually a clover rich ley – and at Chapel Farm these are grazed by sheep or cattle and conserved as big bale silage or big bale hay. The leys are sown in August immediately after grain harvest. Grazing sheep in autumn provides an effective weed control tool in the young leys. Where soil is suitable, potatoes follow the leys instead of the first winter wheat.

The cereals are predominantly winter varieties because, all other factors being equal, they will usually out-yield spring sown cereals. The milling market is the main target. Wheat varieties are selected for disease resistance, grain quality and relative yield potential. Short-strawed varieties have an advantage over longer-strawed varieties in the weed control strategy used at Chapel Farm, since they facilitate the mechanical slicing of tall weed seed-heads.

Varieties currently grown are Malacca and Claire winter wheats and Jalna oats. Oats are grown as a second or third cereal because they demand less fertility than wheat, are competitive against weeds, and also command a reasonable price.

Manurial policy

Soils are analysed on a selective basis, particularly prior to growing potatoes. As indicated above, lime is seldom necessary, but Redzlagg (aluminium calcium phosphate) is occasionally applied, as indicated by soil analysis. Home-produced farmyard manure (plus some imported mushroom compost – based on Chapel Farm wheat straw - and composted household waste) is applied to priority crops, as indicated by soil analysis and when soil conditions permit.

Cereal establishment and weed control

The leys are broken out in late summer by tined tools to dry out the green material. This is then incorporated by ploughing approximately 15 to 20 cm deep, to leave a trash-free surface for the drill. This is a 4 metre wide Roterra combination with 13 rows spaced at 28 cm, plus 46 cm wide tractor wheel spacings for row crop tractor use.

The main perennial weed problems at Chapel Farm are creeping thistle and docks (broad and narrow leaved). Field bindweed is less important and is in any case palatable to sheep. The main annual weeds are charlock and poppies, blackgrass and wild oats, cleavers and chickweed. Less frequent are Scotch thistles, knotgrass and willowherb. Campions, speedwell, fumitory, cranesbill, pansies and scarlet pimpernel are present but in insignificant amounts. Couch grass and brome grass are almost totally confined to field margins.

The relatively high proportion of ley in the rotation contributes to weed control strategy by limiting the opportunity for weed seed build-up in the soil. However, inter-row hoeing constitutes the major element in the weed control strategy. For the first weed control pass, a 4 m wide rear mounted tractor hoe set to match the seed drill uses 10 cm or 12 cm A blades, with side baffles fitted to prevent crop smother. The hoe is fitted with two vertical straight discs which cut grooves in the soil in order to inhibit the hoe from deviating from a straight progress. The light-weight tractor used is articulated, enabling curved headlands to be followed without cutting into the crop. Second and third passes employ 20 cm wide blades, without baffles. Work rate is about 1.6 hectares per hour in larger regular shaped fields. Hoeing operations take place between November and March.

This tractor is also fitted with a front end loader which carries a 4 m wide frame on which hydraulically-powered high speed rotating knives slice off any weed seed heads which project above the crop canopy. These seed heads are usually immature and drop to the ground where they die, but a second flush, of wild oats for instance, may merit a second slicing. Very little crop damage is done by late operations, even though the tractor clearance is unusually low.

In addition to the above mechanical weed control regime, seed cereal crops are hand rogued and occasional dock plants are hand-dug to remove mature plants and to prevent seed return to the soil.

Policy benefits of inter-row hoeing in cereals

Using normal seed rates, plant density is high within these wide spaced rows. This enhances the ability of the crop to compete with any weeds growing within the row. The spaces between rows permit good ventilation and light penetration, whilst the scope for root penetration stimulates compensatory growth of the crop.

Over-wintering weeds on heavy land can become too strongly rooted for good control by comb harrow weeder cultivations. In addition, the hoeing produces a shallow layer of well-aerated tilth which tends to conserve moisture and also mineralises extra nitrogen. This last factor needs further research as protein tends to be lower in wheat grown organically, and this characteristic of the hoeing technique may be a means of reliably enhancing grain protein content.

There have been no lodged crops at Chapel Farm of either wheat or oats grown this way although admittedly the system is most suited to short-strawed varieties. It also facilitates hand-roguing of occasional large weeds and preparation for inspection of crops grown for seed.

One problem which has been experienced with the hoeing technique is caused by not achieving good matching of adjacent seed drill runs. If the outside rows are too far apart, the hoe will not cut all the ground, leaving strips of weeds and if the outside rows are too close together, both rows are destroyed by the hoe. Centre markers are used on the drill and an optical guidance frame is fitted to the tractor windscreen.

Very level and even seedbeds are most desirable for precision management of row cropping. Deep mouldboard ploughing conflicts with this aim, particularly in headland areas. Short stubbles are also desirable as organic straw is in great demand, and surface trash militates against making good clover seedbeds.

There has been a suggestion that row cropping of cereals adversely affects the success of ground nesting birds such as skylarks. Although skylarks are very evident flying over and running along the rows of cereals at Chapel Farm, their nests are extremely difficult to find. Specific research beyond the present monitoring of our farm would be useful in clarifying this aspect.

Pests and diseases

Slugs, aphids and fungal diseases are always present but are not at significant enough levels to affect yield or grain quality. Ergot used to be a problem but is not present now. No direct, reactive techniques are employed to control these pests and diseases, but proactive, preventative strategies include crop rotation and variation in cereal species, selection of disease resistant varieties, high quality seedbeds (e.g. fine, compact seedbeds to reduce slug attack) and vigorous crop rooting and canopy development.

Crop yields and gross margins

Yields of cereals at Chapel Farm average 5 tonnes/hectare for winter wheat and 3.5 t/ha for oats. Typical gross margins are shown in Tables 8.3 and 8.4. Although most of the grain from Chapel Farm is sold into the milling market, it appears that demand is moving strongly towards livestock feed grain, at very similar prices.

Table 8. 3.   Typical gross margin for milling wheat at Chapel Farm

			£/tonne	£/ha	
Output					
	Grain	5t/ha	200	1000	
	Straw	2.5t/ha	35	88	
	Arable Area Payment	£217/ha		217	
	Total output				1305
Variable costs					
	Seed*	220 kg/ha	250	55	
Other (e.g. phosphate)				30	
Total variable costs					85
Gross Margin (£/ha)					1220

*home-saved

Table 8.4.   Typical gross margin for milling oats at Chapel Farm

			£/tonne	£/ha	
Output					
	Grain	3.5t/ha	180	630	
	Straw	2.5t/ha	30	75	
	Arable Area Payment	£217/ha		217	
	Total output				922
Variable costs					
	Seed*	220kg/ha	250	55	
Other (e.g. phosphate)				30	
Total variable costs					85
Gross Margin (£/ha)					837

*home-saved

Chapter 9

Commercial Farm Case Study: Pulses

D. WILSON
Duchy Home Farm, Tetbury, Gloucestershire, GL8 8SE

FARM PROFILE

The Duchy Home Farm comprises 437 hectares of land in-hand plus 324 hectares in share or contract farming arrangements with five neighbouring farms. The altitude ranges from 155 to 190 metres. The soil types vary from typical Cotswold brash with pH values as high as 7.8, through heavy clay, to sandy loams with pH values as low as 5.0. The organic conversion began in 1986 and was completed in 1994.

The enterprises on the farm are as follows:

Livestock:

Dairy	130 Ayrshire cows
Beef	90 Aberdeen Angus suckler cows/heifers
Sheep	550 North Country Mule ewes
Pigs	Camborough/Duroc cross (a local pig specialist's animals on our land)

Crops:

Arable	Winter wheat, spring oats, winter rye, spring beans
Vegetables	Potatoes, carrots and a variety of others for local box scheme

CROP ROTATION

A seven-year crop rotation is followed at Duchy Home Farm:

Year 1→	Yr 2 →	Yr 3→	Yr 4→	Yr 5→	Yr 6→	Yr 7→
G/RC	G/RC	G/RC	WW	SO	SBn	WR

G/RC: Grass/red clover   SBn: Spring beans
WW: Winter wheat   WR: Winter rye
SO: Spring Oats

The rotational sequence is important to the output of the system. The powerhouse of the rotation is three years of clover/grass ley. This is absolutely vital in restoring soil fertility since red clover is capable of fixing between 230 and 460 kg per hectare of nitrogen per annum, as well as improving soil structure. A two-year clover ley is almost as beneficial but a three-year period gives better weed suppression.

The ley is ploughed at the end of Year Three and winter wheat is sown. This is also the time when, in an organic rotation, most nitrogen is leached from the soil. This is a problem that growers are acutely aware of and probably the best solution is to plant spring wheat but, on Cotswold soils in dry summers, this can lead to some unreliable yields. Wheat is the first crop after grass and this is the obvious position for the most exhaustive crop. A catch crop is then sown after the cereal harvest, of stubble turnips, forage rape and mustard. This mops up any residual nitrogen, reduces leaching and keeps the soil covered. It can be either grazed or ploughed under in the late winter or early spring. The land is then ploughed and sown with spring oats, the second crop in the rotation. Again, oats are well-suited to being the second crop as they are lower in their fertility requirement and provide the farm with a good source of high quality feed straw, which is what keeps most of the Aberdeen Angus suckler cows fed throughout the winter.

166

At the end of the second year, the fertility is beginning to drop so this is when the spring beans are sown. We initially sowed beans because a sequence of four cereal crops would be too exhaustive and it was felt that beans would make a good break. Thirteen years ago, when we started growing organic beans, there was little or no margin over the conventional price. Nevertheless, it provided the necessary break to enable us to grow a reasonable crop of rye, which took us to the end of year seven when the clover/grass ley was re-established.

ROLE OF BEANS IN THE FARMING SYSTEM

Beans are an important source of protein at the Duchy Home Farm and are fed to dairy cows and ewes. They are likely to become more important for a number of reasons: Firstly the prohibition on the use of genetically-modified proteins in organic livestock rations is increasing the demand for home-produced organic proteins; secondly the inclusion rates of non-organic feeds in rations are constantly being reduced and are set to disappear completely by 2005. Also there are an increasing number of livestock-only farms that need to purchase their organic proteins or their organic compounded feed containing organic proteins, particularly pig and poultry units. Beans were chosen at the Duchy Home Farm in preference to peas because the land is stony and because they provide a more effective spread of harvest times.

Cultivations and establishment

High quality ploughing is an important first step to getting beans off to a good start. If the soil is on the heavy side, it is best to plough in late winter to achieve a frost mould. Pre-drilling cultivations should move the soil to a depth of 10 to 13 cm to allow deep drill penetration. Something like a Konskilde Vibraflex heavy cultivator is suitable as it leaves the soil ridged up and helps with aeration and drying. This can be left for a few weeks if necessary and does not leave the soil in a vulnerable state. At drilling time, a spring tine or

167

power harrow can be used to level ridges and produce a loose tilth, taking care to avoid compaction.

If conditions allow, beans should be planted from mid-February onwards. The seed should be sown as deep as possible – the seed is large so it is difficult to plant it too deep – with a covering of at least 7 cm of settled soil. Drilling also offers an opportunity to tramline for the weeder, allowing more accurate driving which is useful with wider machines. Ploughing beans under is the method usually used for winter beans but can also be used for spring sown varieties, particularly if planting early where rooks are a problem (deeper seed is harder to reach). The disadvantage with ploughing down the seed is that the seed distribution is less even. This is not a problem with winter beans because they tiller well. Spring beans do not have this power to compensate, and thinly seeded patches will stay thin and open, which can allow weeds to develop quickly.

There is a lot of variation in seed size between varieties so it is important to check the thousand seed weight to ensure that the right number is being planted. Sixty seeds per square metre are about right; the more traditional 40 to 50 seeds is too low especially in dry summers. Up to a certain point, there is a direct correlation between the volume of haulm and crop yield, i.e. more haulm equals more yield. Too high a seed rate will cause the plants to compete with each other, producing tall leafy growth with fewer pods. This, in turn, leads to more disease and to lodging, a point that is often clearly illustrated on headland overlaps.

Choice of variety

This is a bit of a nightmare because the great variability in this plant can mean that the NIAB (National Institute of Agricultural Botany) figures are a little meaningless.

The aim should be to grow a spring bean that is tall, so that it competes with weeds, stands well and has good disease resistance.

Low-tannin types are theoretically what we should be growing because they can be included in livestock rations at higher rates. The problem with these white flowered varieties is that they tend to be very short, unreliable in yield and more disease prone.

Varieties come and go from the NIAB recommended list with great rapidity, which means that, just as an 'old favourite' is becoming established, it becomes unobtainable. One option is to clean your own seed, which will keep varieties going for longer but it should be tested for germination and for the seed-borne disease *Ascochyta fabae.*

Manurial policy

Farm yard manure (FYM) is only applied to land while it is in the 3-year clover/grass phase and slurry is spread on silage leys before and between silage cuts. The normal rate of application for both FYM and slurry is about 12.5 t/ha. All FYM is tipped in long windrows and turned frequently in order to encourage composting and allow heating, which dramatically reduces pathogens and weed seed viability. It is spread within a year to minimise nutrient losses.

Soils are analysed twice during the 7-year rotation and lime is applied where needed.

Weed control

Beans are undoubtedly one of the dirtier crops to grow so a positive approach is needed. If the intended field for beans has known weed problems, it may be preferable to grow them elsewhere. Blind harrowing (i.e. pre-emergence) 10 to 14 days after planting is a very worthwhile start.

The weeder should then be run through the crop 4 to 5 times at two-week intervals, when the soil is dry and in sunshine, preferably before the weeds are beyond the cotyledon stage. The tine angle should be set severely – bean plants are surprisingly resilient and will recover completely within a few hours.

Pests and diseases

Chocolate spot: mainly a problem in winter beans but can be seen in very early sown spring varieties.
Bean rust: usually appears late in season in hot dry weather but does not often threaten the crop.
Downy mildew: this can cause problems and is best avoided by growing resistant varieties.
Black bean aphid: usually avoided in garden broad beans by pinching out the tops – slightly more difficult on a field scale. Ladybirds, flower bugs and other predatory insects will remove them in field crops.

Harvesting and drying

The crop starts to ripen from the bottom up when the leaves drop off and the pods turn black and become brittle. Once the whole plant has darkened, it is ready to combine. Harvesting takes place from late August to mid-September, which means that beans do not clash with the combining of other crops. They are normally easy to harvest, the big heavy seed is easily threshed from the pod and, because of its weight, combine wind speed settings are high, giving a relatively clean sample. It is not necessary to worry about one or two green beans in the trailer, they will become as dry as the ones surrounding them – waiting until every single bean is stone hard could mean harvest is a Yuletide affair.

The moisture content at which beans should be stored and sold is 14%. Obviously, the ideal way to get to this moisture content is in the field and, in dry summers, this is easy to achieve. When drying is necessary a continuous flow dryer should be used, taking care not to dry the crop too fast. It is easy to heat the outside of the bean while the centre remains cool, which leads to cracking.

If the moisture content is above 20%, it is better to dry the beans twice. On-the-floor drying will not crack the beans and is an altogether gentler system but requires more careful management. A ventilated floor is best, but on-floor ducts are fine provided they are not too far apart. Beans piled in a heap provide less air resistance than cereals, which means that the air will tend to rush to the top and escape quickly. Air-flow must therefore be checked to ensure that it is even over the whole surface and the heap should be level.

Yields and gross margins

Since 1995 bean yields have varied between 1.2 and 3.2 t/ha. At the same time prices for organic beans have increased from £157/t to about £235/t and gross margins have ranged between £540/ha and £880/ha. An estimated gross margin for the 2001 crop is given in Table 9.1.

Table 9.1.   Estimated gross margin for 2001 for spring beans at Duchy Home Farm.

		£/tonne	£/ha
Output			
Seed	2.75 t/ha	235	646
Arable Area Payment	£268/ha		268
Total output			914
Variable costs			
Seed*	216 kg/ha	350	75
Total variable costs			75
Gross Margin (£/ha)			839

*blend of Maris Bead and Titch

FUTURE DEVELOPMENTS

The farm is assessing the usefulness of different variety blends and crop mixtures. At present a blend of two bean varieties is being evaluated and this may be extended to three varieties in the future. A mixture of beans, wheat, barley and oats for harvesting by combine, milling and feeding as one crop may be tried. Undersowing of beans with clover is also a possibility. It appears that soaking beans before feeding, instead of milling them, may increase their nutritional value and this may be done if a simple method can be developed on a large enough scale for the dairy herd.